The Structure and Function of Animal Cell Components

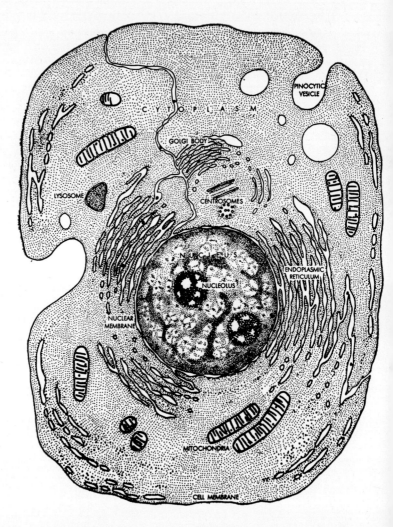

Modern diagram of a typical cell based on what is seen in electron micrographs. (From J. Brachet, *Scientific American*, September 1961.)

The Structure and Function of Animal Cell Components

AN INTRODUCTORY TEXT

by

P. N. CAMPBELL

*Reader in Biochemistry, Courtauld Institute of Biochemistry,
The Middlesex Hospital Medical School, London*

with the assistance and collaboration of

M. A. EPSTEIN

*Reader in Experimental Pathology, Bland Sutton Institute
of Pathology, The Middlesex Hospital Medical School,
London*

PERGAMON PRESS

OXFORD · LONDON · EDINBURGH · NEW YORK
TORONTO · SYDNEY · PARIS · BRAUNSCHWEIG

Pergamon Press Ltd., Headington Hill Hall, Oxford
4 & 5 Fitzroy Square, London W.1

Pergamon Press (Scotland) Ltd., 2 & 3 Teviot Place, Edinburgh 1

Pergamon Press Inc., 44–01 21st Street, Long Island City, New York 11101

Pergamon of Canada, Ltd., 6 Adelaide Street East, Toronto, Ontario

Pergamon Press (Aust.) Pty. Ltd., 20–22 Margaret Street, Sydney,
New South Wales

Pergamon Press S.A.R.L., 24 rue des Écoles, Paris 5ᵉ

Vieweg & Sohn GmbH, Burgplatz 1, Braunschweig

Printed in Great Britain by Page Bros. (Norwich) Ltd., Norwich

Contents

v

Preface

SCIENTISTS, like most other groups of workers, have tended to specialize and to segregate themselves into subdisciplines. Those who were interested in the application of scientific principles to medicine were no exception to this rule so that instead of the two scientific subjects on which the main emphasis was placed, formerly anatomy and physiology, there have now arisen many more, represented, for example, by biochemistry, microbiology, and immunology, to mention only a few.

One of the most interesting recent developments has been the tendency for these more recent subdivisions to be blurred so that the various subdisciplines have become less well defined. A stimulus for this development has been the coming of "molecular biology". This subject has cut across the existing subdivisions and drawn together all those who are interested in explaining the processes of life at the molecular level. Thus scientists trained initially in widely different fields have found themselves as colleagues. Many of the most significant contributions to molecular biology have come from those who specialized in physics during their first degree. First the physicists applied physical methods to biological problems but soon they found themselves fascinated by all aspects of biology. The result of this is that the artificiality of the former barriers has been revealed and there is now a realization that over-specialization can inhibit progress. The recent removal of barriers has had a profound effect not only on research but also in the present teaching at universities. Thus many of the new universities in this country have set up broad faculties of biology and molecular science and the days of numerous isolated departments seem to be over.

An excellent example of the fruits of collaboration between scientists trained in different disciplines is the subject of this monograph. The method of the physiologist is to study the functioning of the organs of the body, either in the intact animal or in a treated animal or in the isolated organs. In all these situations the cells remain intact. The biochemist aims to make a closer inspection of the situation and therefore often brutally treats the tissues either by slicing them into thin sections or by mincing them. In such preparations many of the cells remain intact but many are also damaged and in all cases some at least of the properties of the original organ are lost. Undoubtedly, some biochemists have been guilty in the past of drawing conclusions from the results of the application of such methods which did not take account of the way in which their experimental preparations differed from the intact animal. As a result physiologists were often critical of this approach and unfortunately the two disciplines have tended to move apart. Perhaps even more regrettable was the fact that biochemists were missing many opportunities and thereby wasting a good deal of effort.

The next approach of the biochemist was to attempt to destroy the structure of the cells of the tissue by grinding and to produce a so-called homogenate. Even the biochemists themselves complained that the product was not homogeneous but the name has persisted to describe a mixture of undamaged cells, damaged cells and their contents in various stages of disruption. When the metabolism of such homogenates was studied and conclusions drawn as to the way in which the cells performed *in vivo* the wrath and pity of the cytologists was aroused. In spite of this a good deal of progress in understanding metabolic pathways was achieved.

As a result of this second round of criticism the biochemist learnt to break up cells under more carefully controlled conditions and with a greater appreciation of what he was about. It is this aspect of the work of biochemists that has been an important area of development in recent years.

The other side of the story concerns the cytologist, anatomist and pathologist. The cytologist is interested in the internal structure of the cell and the way in which the different structures contribute to the overall function of the particular cell. The world of the cytologist took on a completely new dimension with the advent of the electron microscope. Until the development of this instrument many of the morphological structures in the cytoplasm remained a mystery as reference to any diagram of the cell in an older textbook will demonstrate (see below). Not only had the electron microscope itself to be developed but means had to be devised to make preparations which were sufficiently thin to allow penetration by an electron beam.

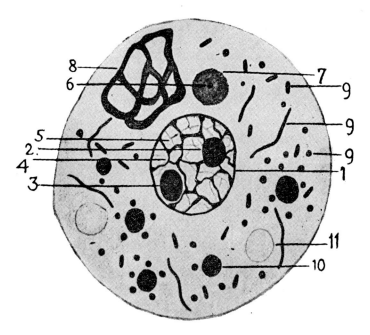

DIAGRAM OF CELL. [From *The Essentials of Histology*, 16th edn. (Ed. by H. M. Carleton and R. H. D. Short), Longmans, London, 1954.]

As a result of the development of techniques for the application of electron microscopy to cells it is now realized that the cytoplasm is highly organized and contains a highly intricate network of structures. It is at this point that the biochemist joins the cytologist. This monograph is about the correlation between the morphological structures as revealed by cytologists, and their function as determined by biochemists. It represents, therefore, the results of fruitful collaboration between scientists of two very different disciplines.

I have written assuming that the reader has an elementary knowledge of both biochemistry and cytology. In the space available I have been unable to do more than introduce the subject which covers a very wide field. In selecting material I have naturally tended to dwell on the subjects with which I am more familiar and am acutely aware of how much has been omitted. Although I have included a good deal of biochemistry, some of it rather elementary, I have tried to limit it to that which is required to illustrate the significance of the morphology. I am indeed most fortunate to have had the help and guidance of Dr. Epstein who has a wealth of experience of fields other than my own. Dr. Whittaker offered many valuable criticisms of the first draft of Chapter 2.

At the end of each chapter will be found references not only to the significant original publications but also suggestions for further reading. The bibliography is by no means comprehensive but I hope that it may lead the reader to more extensive reviews which contain a fuller list of references to the original literature.

Finally, I should like to thank all those authors and publishers who have allowed me to reproduce their diagrams and electron micrographs. I can only hope that I have interpreted their publications correctly and given credit where it was due. In the case of the many electron micrographs reproduced from the *Journal of Cell Biology* I state, as requested, that some loss of quality in the process of reproduction is inevitable so that the results are not representative of the originals.

I am also greatly indebted to Mr. A. N. Drury (the medical artist of the hospital) for the original diagrams, and the Photographic Department for their unfailing help.

CHAPTER 1

Introduction

THE object of this chapter is to fill in the background which is necessary before the more detailed information contained in the later chapters can be appreciated. First it is necessary to understand the functions of cells, then the nature of their fine structure and finally the various approaches that can be made to correlate structure and function.

Function of Cells

The functions may be of two general types which we may designate physiological and biochemical.

Physiological

In a bacterium or other unicellular organism the function of the cell is entirely selfish in that its object is to survive and if possible to grow and to reproduce. In multicellular organisms the cells are differentiated so that in addition to the activities already mentioned each has one or more additional special functions which contribute to the well-being or activities of the organism as a whole. The only true exception to this rule would seem to be the tumour cell which aims only at its own growth and does this at the expense of the normal cells of the host. Tumour cells may also possess some properties that are inherited from the cells of the tissue of origin, but this is merely an incidental attribute. An example of such a phenomenon is found in adenomas of the adrenal gland where the tumour cells are often very active in the synthesis of those steroid hormones normally synthesized by the adrenal gland itself.

In the case of normal cells which constitute the various organs and tissues of the body the fundamental functions of survival and the performance of special activities are naturally of prime importance. Linked to these is the function of growth which is especially important when the animal itself is in an active phase or the young are *in utero*; perhaps less obvious is the amount of tissue damage that must be repaired. Not only is this because the animal suffers wounds but many of the cells, such as those that line the intestinal wall, are constantly being broken down and replaced by others. A more obvious situation in which to observe this is the continual replacement of the protective covering of the animal in the form of skin.

Experimentally, it is sometimes possible to arrange especially interesting examples of the functioning of this repair mechanism as when two-thirds of the liver of a rat is removed by surgery. After this operation the liver rapidly grows again so that its original weight, although not shape, is recovered in about three weeks. In such cases the process of replication and growth of the liver cells can be speeded up and a very useful and interesting source of experimental material is available. Another example is the removal of limb buds during the larval stages of various amphibia.

The above functions may be regarded as almost entirely internal in the economy of the cell. We must now discuss those other functions that affect the well-being of the animal as a whole and which are typical of differentiated cells. These may be classified broadly into two groups. In the first are the functions performed by the cell which do not involve the export or secretion of any substance. Thus the reticulocytes and especially their progenitors, the bone marrow cells, synthesize haemoglobin and this, of course, has an essential role in the economy of the animal. These cells do not, however, export the haemoglobin but make it function within themselves. Muscle cells synthesize myosin and adenosine triphosphate (ATP) and use these substances to make the muscle perform its function of contraction when necessary. The liver cells perform many functions which come within this group. One thinks of the storage of carbohydrate in the form of the polysaccharide glycogen (which is paralleled in the plant by the formation of starch and amylopectin). The monosaccharide, glucose, is converted to glycogen and the latter is broken down again to glucose 1-phosphate. The whole process, involving as it does many enzymic reactions, is carefully controlled to ensure that the concentration of the blood sugar remains sufficiently constant. Another function of the liver cell is to "detoxicate", or render harmless, substances that would otherwise damage or upset the metabolism of the body. Thus benzoic acid, present in prepared foodstuffs as a preservative, is converted in the liver to benzoylglycine (hippuric acid) and is excreted in the urine as such. This brings us to our final example, that of the phagocytes, which engulf many kinds of material, particularly dead cells, and act as the scavengers of the body.

The second type of communal activity involves the cell in the production of a substance which is itself of benefit to the animal. There are many examples of this kind but the ones that immediately come to mind are as follows. The exocrine cells of the pancreas make and export a wide variety of enzymes that play an essential role in the degradation of foodstuffs in the intestinal tract. Such enzymes are present in the pancreatic juice which flows into the duodenum. These enzymes catalyse the breakdown of carbohydrate, protein, nucleic acids and lipids and are known collectively as "hydrolytic" enzymes. Examples are amylase, trypsin, chymotrypsin, ribonuclease, and lipase. Since the cells themselves are made of protein, carbohydrate and lipid the production and excretion of such lethal materials is a difficult feat. In the case of some enzymes such as chymotrypsin and trypsin the enzyme itself is made and exported from the cell in an inactive form known as a "zymogen" and is then converted into the active form in the duodenum. So far nothing is known of the way in which the other enzymes are excreted but we shall be able to discuss the morphological aspects of this fascinating process at a later stage.

The liver perhaps has an easier job in this respect for the proteins that it makes and exports are not potentially lethal. All the proteins contained in the plasma of animals are made by the liver cell with the exception of γ-globulin, the protein that contains antibodies. This protein is made by the plasma cells which are present in the lymph nodes and which are stimulated by the presence of antigen. Quantitatively, the most important protein made by the liver is serum albumin which forms about 60–80% of the plasma protein.

Another cell type that is particularly active in synthesizing protein is that of the mammary gland. The cells of this tissue are brought rapidly into action after parturition and they then synthesize large quantities of milk protein for the sustenance of the young. In the case of egg formation in birds, the protein that is stored up for the later use of the young may either be synthesized by the oviduct, as with ovalbumin, or by the liver from whence it is transferred to the egg, as with phosvitin.[1]

Finally, there are those cells which produce protein for the protection of the animal. This protein is mainly keratin and may take the form of nails or hair. The problem of making and secreting such an insoluble protein must be immense and perhaps it is not surprising that in the case of hair, the follicles sometimes give up their unequal task before the death of the animal. The process of hair formation is under an interesting form of control for at times of moulting the hair is lost and then there must be a period of rapid replacement activity.

The liver is a good example of an organ that contains a variety of cell types. The predominant cell is the parenchymal but this only represents about 60% of the total mass. The next most important cell in the liver is the Kupffer cell which is concerned with the reticulo-endothelial system. We have already mentioned that the phagocytes and the Kupffer cells have a similar scavenging function. These particular cells are so efficient that if Indian ink is injected intravenously, granules of the pigment are found shortly afterwards in the Kupffer cells. Finally, the liver is the site of synthesis of the bile which is stored in the gall-bladder before being secreted by way of the bile duct into the duodenum. Thus in addition to parenchymal cells and Kupffer cells there are cells lining the bile duct.

This brief consideration of the different cells contained within the liver may serve as a reminder to biochemists that it is not right to assume that all tissues are homogeneous as regards cell type. Indeed this is a rather rare phenomenon. It is usually virtually impossible to separate the different cell types in a tissue but the possibility that the result of various treatments to an animal could lead to a change in the population of the cells of, say the liver, is usually completely ignored by biochemists.

Biochemical

Naturally, there is no clear-cut difference between the biochemical and the physiological function of a cell but in this section we will briefly consider cell function from a chemical standpoint.

The fundamental assumption which underlies the basis of all biochemical thought, and which is amply supported by fact, is that there is an essential unity in the chemistry of all living things regardless of their place in the plant or animal kingdom. The prime example of this belief is the common currency in which energy is handled in all forms of life. I refer, of course, to ATP. The utilization of food materials by living organisms proceeds via specific sequences of enzymic reactions collectively described as metabolic pathways which fulfil two main functions: they supply the precursors of cell constituents, and they supply the energy necessary for biosynthetic and other endergonic processes to occur. In either case it is ATP which is the form in which the chemical energy is used by the cell.

Nutrients come to a cell in a wide variety of forms. Many microorganisms can exist solely on acetate although often some more reduced compound such as ethanol is also present. However, glucose would be a more natural nutrient. If a macromolecule such as cellulose were provided, the bacteria would attempt to provide an enzyme which would break it down to units of glucose. Plants depend mainly on photosynthesis which means CO_2 and the energy derived from the sun. Using these sources they build up glucose. Higher animals can utilize the same low molecular weight substances directly but generally they feed on more complex materials and break them down to glucose, amino acids and fatty acids before absorption from the gut. Often in the higher animals bacteria play an important part in such a process so that, for example, in the rabbit, but not in man, cellulose yields glucose because of the intestinal flora. In ruminants the rumen is a most important site for the breakdown of the great variety of food that is ingested. In this case bacteria play an essential role and the major end-product is acetate which is a convenient metabolic substrate.

While, therefore, there are certain differences in the nature of the nutrients available to various organisms, the nutrients that actually reach the cell are remarkably similar. The next barrier the nutrient has to overcome is that of the membrane surrounding the cell. This has a remarkable property, protecting the cell against unwanted material and controlling the flow of the wanted substances. Once inside, we shall see that in animal cells, there is a special organelle or subcellular particle that is assigned the task of converting the energy contained within the C–C links of the nutrient into ATP. In animal cells this is done by the mitochondrion and in plants by the chloroplast. In the mitochondrion we shall see that nearly all the ATP is synthesized as the result of the operation of a metabolic cycle in each turn of which every molecule of acetate yields 2 moles of CO_2 and water and 12 moles of ATP, the amount of each constituent of the cycle not being affected as a result of its operation.

With the exception of red blood cells, all types of cell in an animal contain mitochondria and the metabolism of all mitochondria is believed to be the same irrespective of the type of cell in which they occur. The only differences between the cell types in this respect would seem to concern the number of mitochondria per cell.

In the case of protein synthesis we believe again that all proteins are made by basically the same metabolic mechanism irrespective of the origin of the cell. All proteins are made from free amino acids and there are a maximum of twenty from which to choose. In not all cases are the maximum number of variants used; in the case of gelatin, for example, no tryptophan is present. Also in some proteins an additional amino acid seems to have been added but it is now realized that an amino acid may be modified after it has been inserted in peptide linkage. Collagen is characterized by the presence of hydroxy-proline and this is formed from proline after the peptide has been formed.

The substance in each cell that controls the nature of the protein which is synthesized by it, is the deoxyribonucleic acid (DNA) which is contained in the nucleus of the cell. Since the DNA of all the cells in a given animal is identical it follows that there must be a way in which the potential information residing in the DNA of a cell is either suppressed or expressed.

The other major cell constituents are, of course, the carbohydrates and the lipids. Here again the pathways of metabolism in each cell are basically the same but different examples of these substances will be found in the various cells. Thus lactose is only found in the milk. This suggests that the enzymes responsible for the synthesis of these substances have an unequal distribution and this is undoubtedly true. Not only this but two enzymes fulfilling an identical function in two different types of cells are often slightly different in physical properties when isolated.

Finally, we must mention the activity of the chemical messengers or hormones which are produced by the ductless glands at the behest of the pituitary gland in the brain. The secretions of the pituitary are characterized by the fact that they are often very specific in their effect on different cells. Thus thyrotropin acts only on the thyroid, and adrenocorticotrophic hormone on the cortex of the adrenal. Other hormones, the activity of which are controlled by the specific secretions of the pituitary, are in contrast rather general in their action. Thyroxine, released from the thyroid gland, stimulates the metabolism of many cells and the role of insulin, although not clearly understood, is also a general one.

Although endocrinologists, who specialize in the study of the action of hormones, now have a fairly good idea of the physiological effects of these substances, they know very little of the way in which the effects are mediated at the molecular level. But the fact is that cells differ markedly in their susceptibility to hormones and no doubt it is due to this that these substances can exert such a fine control over the metabolism of the whole animal. Probably the cells least affected by hormones are those of tumours although even here there are exceptions.

Structure of Cells

Virtually all animal cells can be divided into two parts, the nucleus and the cytoplasm. The only exception to this general rule is provided by the mammalian reticulocyte which is derived from a nucleated cell, the erythroblast. The nucleus of the cell contains the genetic material which determines the activity and general properties of the cell and also plays an essential role in cell division ensuring that the daughter cells carry the same genetic information. In the event of a mutation, which means a change in the genetic make-up of the cell, this must initially involve the nucleus.

Although the nucleus is of great importance it is not the site in the cell at which protein, glycogen or lipids are made or energy produced from incoming nutrients. These are the roles of the cytoplasm. Apart from certain secretory granules the largest morphological constituent of the cytoplasm is the mitochondrion. As has been mentioned and will be explained in detail, it is in these organelles that energy is produced and they can, therefore, be thought of collectively as the power house of the cell. Other particles that can be identified in the cytoplasm are the lysosomes and microbodies which are packets of enzymes.

A very important component of the cytoplasm not so far mentioned consists of a complex system of interconnecting membranes composing the endoplasmic reticulum and the small electron dense particles, the ribosomes, which may or may not be associated with it. If the membranes have ribosomes attached to them then the system is known as the rough surfaced endoplasmic reticulum, whereas in the absence of ribosomes, it is designated smooth surfaced endoplasmic reticulum. All cells also contain areas in which the smooth reticulum is arranged in a rather intricate and characteristic pattern and in this case it is known as the Golgi "zone", "complex" or "apparatus".

We have already mentioned that ribosomes may be attached to

the membranes but there are some cells in which membranes are absent but which still contain ribosomes. Such a cell is the reticulocyte, active in the synthesis of haemoglobin. In the liver cell most of the ribosomes are membrane bound but some are "free".

When the cells of the liver are disrupted and the components are separated according to their density, as explained later, the lightest fraction is designated the "microsomes". This fraction will contain varying proportions of fragments of the rough and smooth reticulum and free ribosomes. In the case of the reticulocyte the microsome fraction will contain only ribosomes without membranes.

A typical example of the parenchymal cell of the liver is seen in Plate I.1, which is a low power electron micrograph that shows most of the components mentioned above. The fine structure of these components is seen clearly in Plate I.2. This shows that the nuclear envelope consists of a double membrane which is interrupted by pores. The folding of the inner membrane of the mitochondria is seen. These are the so-called cristae and are characteristic of mitochondria. The two different arrangements of ribosomes are also clearly seen as is the rough and smooth endoplasmic reticulum. The cell membranes of two adjacent cells are apparent with the bile duct canuliculi running between.[2] Table 1.1 gives a rather different kind of analysis of the rat liver cell and represents calculations made from both biochemical and morphological data by Professor Drabkin showing an approximate quantitative analysis of the cell.

While the liver cell contains most of the constituents found in cells in general, it also illustrates a particular kind of cell with specialized functions. Another kind of specialization is indicated by the exocrine cells of the pancreas which, as has been explained, synthesize and export large quantities of hydrolytic enzymes. Plate I.3 shows the fine structure of such a cell containing zymogen granules. The origin of these organelles has been studied by Palade and Siekevitz at the Rockefeller Institute in New York (see Chapter 4).

Another cell that has been much studied recently is that of the brain, from which Whittaker and his colleagues have succeeded in isolating various components.[3]

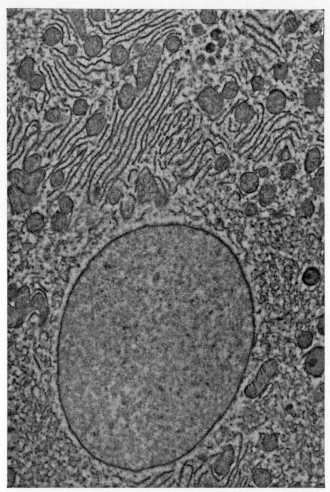

PLATE I.1. Survey picture of part of a parenchymal rat liver cell. The nucleus is seen bottom centre. The cytoplasm is filled with several stacks of rough surfaced endoplasmic reticulum in parallel array together with numerous mitochondria. Microbodies with dense eccentric nucleoides can also be seen as well as smaller dense lysosomes. Magnification × 10,000. (Electron micrograph by courtesy of M. A. Epstein and R. M. Hicks, Bland Sutton Institute of Pathology, The Middlesex Hospital Medical School.)

TABLE 1.1. THE RAT LIVER CELL
(Calculations made by Professor Drabkin)

Liver cell	Diameter	$19\cdot3\mu$
	Volume	3081 μ^3 (as tetrakaideca-hedron)
	Number per gram	$3\cdot25 \times 10^8$
Nuclei	Diameter	$7\cdot7\ \mu$
	Volume	239 μ^3
	Nuclear fraction	$7\cdot76\%$
	Number per cell	$1\cdot0$ (assumed)
Mitochondria	Diameter	$0\cdot35\ \mu$ to $1\cdot2\ \mu$ (mean = $0\cdot83\ \mu$)
plus	Volume	Volume, as prolate spheroid for mean of $0\cdot83\ \mu = 0\cdot484\ \mu^3$
Lysosomes	Mitochondrial fraction	$21\cdot1\%$
	Number per cell	Mean = 1343
Microsomes	Fraction of Cell	$10\cdot85\%$
Ribosomes	Diameters	$0\cdot023\ \mu = 230\text{Å}$ and $0\cdot0140\ \mu$ (140Å) major and minor axes respectively of oblate spheroid
	Volume	$3\cdot871 \times 10^{-6}\ \mu^3$
	Fraction of cell	$1\cdot04\%$
	Number per cell	
	Calc. by e.m.	$8\cdot65 \times 10^6$
	Calc. from RNA	$8\cdot19 \times 10^6$

Methods of Correlating the Fine Structure and Function of Cells

Having discussed the function of cells and then briefly the structures that they contain it is now necessary to survey the methods that are at our disposal for correlating the two. These methods can be subdivided into three: comparison of the fine structure of various cells with differing functions; cytochemistry; and methods involving the disruption of the cell and the isolation of the components.

Comparative

Cytologists have for long compared the fine structure of an enormous variety of cells and tried to correlate their findings with the function of the cells. An early success using this method was that of Palade[4] concerning the function of the rough endoplasmic

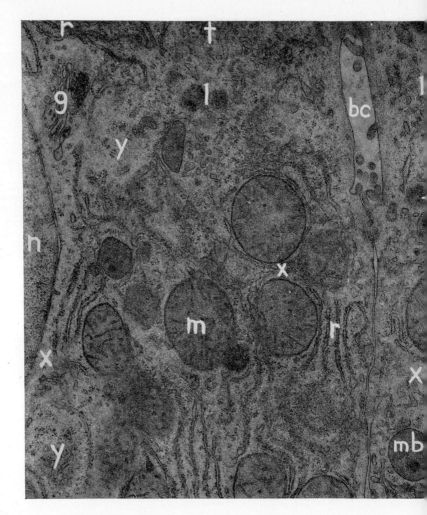

PLATE I.2. Survey electron micrograph showing parts of two adjacent rat liver parenchymal cells. The nucleus (*n*) of one lies on the left of the field bounded by its double envelope which is interrupted by several pores. The intracellular border runs from top to bottom on the right of the field and includes in its upper part a bile canaliculus (*bc*) into which microvilli protrude. The cytoplasm contains numerous mitochondria (*m*), microbodies (*mb*) and lysosomes (*l*). In addition, stacks of rough surfaced endoplasmic reticulum (*r*),

reticulum. The amount of this component varies enormously between different types of cell, whereas all cells active in protein synthesis have a large number of ribosomes in one form or another. Palade came to the conclusion there was a reasonably close correlation between the amount of rough endoplasmic reticulum and the relative importance among the functions of the particular cell of the synthesis of protein for export. Thus the reticulocyte has no rough endoplasmic reticulum but many free ribosomes whereas the exocrine cell of the pancreas has the reverse situation.

Many similar attempts have been made to assign a function to the smooth endoplasmic reticulum. At first it appeared to be concerned in the liver with the synthesis of glycogen but this idea has not been sustained. It is now clear that the smooth reticulum plays an important part in the synthesis of lipids and steroids.

The number of mitochondria in a cell seems to correlate well with its metabolic activity so that, coincident with the work of biochemists, cytologists were also satisfied that mitochondria were important sites of energy production.

Cytochemistry

Cytochemical methods depend on the identification of substances within the organization of the cell by utilizing their characteristic chemical properties. The original techniques involved the formation of coloured reaction products. Thus the tissue is sectioned, fixed to maintain its morphology and stained with the reagent. Examples of this technique that will be discussed later are the Feulgen reaction for DNA and the periodic acid–Schiff reaction (PAS reaction) for carbohydrate. Similar methods have been developed to enable the positions of enzymes to be located in the cell.

Golgi elements (*g*) and smooth tubules of the endoplasmic reticulum (*t*), can be seen; at *x* rough and smooth elements of this system are continuous. Ribosomes are both attached to the rough endoplasmic reticulum and free in the cytoplasm as at *y*. Magnification × 22,000. (Electron micrograph by courtesy of M. A. Epstein and R. M. Hicks, Bland Sutton Institute of Pathology, The Middlesex Hospital Medical School.)

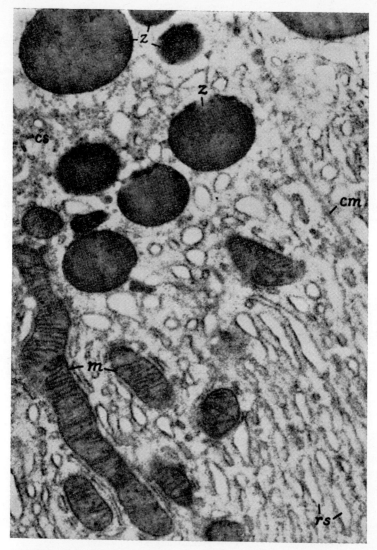

PLATE I.3. Part of an exocrine cell from the pancreas of the guinea-pig. The base region of the cell occupies the lower half of the figure and characteristically contains a few mitochondrial profiles (*m*) and numerous profiles of the endoplasmic reticulum (*rs*) which belong

Thus the so-called Gomori procedure can be used for the detection of acid phosphatase. In this β-glycerophosphate is used as the substrate and is hydrolysed by the enzyme at pH5, the phosphate ions liberated being deposited as lead phosphate due to the presence of lead nitrate. The lead phosphate is then converted to lead sulphide which is dark brown–black. Unfortunatley, most of the enzymes to which this technique is applicable catalyse hydrolytic reactions with a rather broad specificity of substrate and they are probably not the most interesting group of enzymes. Further examples of this technique will be discussed in Chapter 5.

A variation of the above methods was devised by the American cytologist Coons from Boston to enable antibodies and antigens to be identified in cells. In this procedure an antibody to a cell constituent is prepared and is then rendered fluorescent by the attachment of an appropriate reagent such as fluorescein. A section of the cell is prepared and the fluorescent antibody allowed to react with the antigen within it. After a suitable washing procedure the section is examined under the microscope and the presence of antigen revealed by the fluorescent stain. A modification of the technique allows for the detection in the cells of antibody instead of antigen.

The methods so far discussed all involve the detection of a coloured or fluorescent substance in the tissue section so that they depend on the use of light microscopy. Valuable as these methods are it is often desirable to be able to locate substances more precisely than can be done by methods depending on light microscopy alone and so in recent years a number of techniques which utilize the greater definition of electron microscopy have been developed. These methods necessarily depend on the deposition of electron dense substances that may be identified in electron micrographs. An

---

to the rough surfaced types and are dispersed in more or less parallel rows. The apical region of the cell (upper part of the figure) is occupied by a few circular profiles of zymogen granules (z) with dense content consisting of stored digestive enzymes and enzyme precursors. Elements of the endoplasmic reticulum appear at random among the zymogen granules. Magnification $\times$ 31,000. [From G. E. Palade, in *Microsomal Particles and Protein Synthesis*, pp. 36–61 (Ed. Roberts), Pergamon Press, Oxford, 1958.]

example of these methods is the application of the Gomori reaction by Holt and his colleagues. The precise deposition of the lead-containing electron opaque precipitate enables acid phosphatase to be located in the fine structure of the cell.[5]

The Coons fluorescent antibody technique can be adapted to electron microscopy by utilizing the electron dense properties of the iron-containing protein, ferritin. Not only can the presence of ferritin in its natural environment "the parenchymal liver cell" be detected but ferritin can be coupled to other proteins, particularly antibodies, so that it can be used as a marker for proteins other than ferritin itself.[6]

Radioactively-labelled substances may also be used in cytochemistry. One of the most elegant uses of this technique is for detecting the synthesis of DNA in cells. The cells are incubated with tritium-labelled thymidine which is incorporated into the nucleic acid. The cells are then placed on a photographic emulsion and the presence of tritium locates the newly synthesized DNA. A similar method can be used with other radioactive isotopes such as iodine-131 and carbon-14 but tritium has the advantage that the path of its β particles is short so that the definition of its location is relatively precise. For this reason tritium is used in studies involving electron microscopy. Thin sections of the tissue containing the isotope are prepared and left in contact with photographic emulsion. After development the sandwich consisting of both emulsion and section is examined under the electron microscope. The microscope is focused to reveal both the fine structure of the tissue and the silver grains of the emulsion. This is difficult to achieve because of the limited depth of focus of the microscope; moreover the fine structure tends to be obscured by the presence of emulsion.

It will be realized from these examples that cytochemical methods have great value wherever they can be applied. In many ways they are more satisfactory than the methods to be described in the next section, for the organization of the cell under examination is not fundamentally disturbed. Fixation does, however, cause considerable trouble and the localization of a very soluble substance such as albumin is likely to be difficult. Hence, if one does not find a substance in the cell section it does not mean that it was not there originally. At present the application of these methods is still rather limited but it is a rapidly growing field of study.

Disruption

In the two previous methods the organization of the cell was left relatively undisturbed while various observations were made on it. We now come to a much more brutal method involving as it does the partial destruction of the cell structure and an attempt to determine the properties of the degradation products. Ideally the object is to break up the cell and release the constituents in a way that will leave them unaffected. This is, of course, an impossible demand especially when the nature of the endoplasmic reticulum is considered, for this constituent is not particulate but is a complex network of membranes which it would be impossible to release *in toto*. We have first, therefore, to consider the various ways in which a cell may be disrupted. This may be by utilizing the effect of grinding, of ultrasonic vibrations or making use of the osmotic properties of cells which often swell and burst if the conditions are not isotonic.

Grinding can be done in a variety of ways but for the reasons already explained the method of choice is that which is most gentle. This usually involves different types of glass or plastic-and-glass homogenizers. The classical version known as the Potter homogenizer is shown in Fig. 1.1. In this method the tissue is usually cut up finely with scissors or in a crude mincer and placed in the mortar with some buffered salt solution. The pestle is rotated either by hand or on a motor and is worked up and down in the mortar. The degree of disintegration is governed by the clearance between mortar and pestle, the speed of rotation of the pestle and the number of times it is moved up and down. For some purposes it is satisfactory to aim at the total breakdown of all the cells in the tissue but in other cases this would cause too much destruction of the organelles released.

Variations of the Potter homogenizer in which the glass pestle is

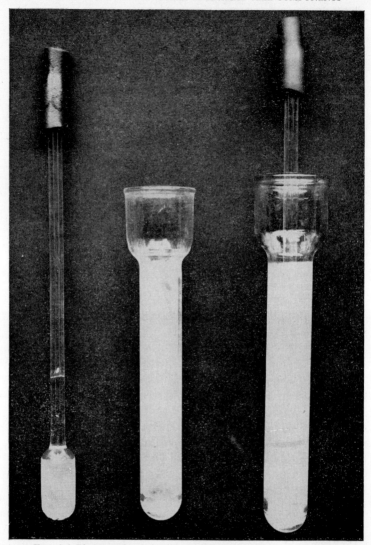

FIG. 1.1 Photograph of the "Potter" homogenizer for disrupting tissues and cells. The glass pestle is rotated in the glass mortar usually by connecting the pestle to a motor by rubber tubing.

replaced by Teflon or the whole apparatus is made in precision bore Perspex are popular for particular purposes and it is probably true that almost every worker has his own individual preference. In one form or another, therefore, this is the most commonly used apparatus for the disruption of cells but unfortunately it is not suitable for all tissues. It is best for soft tissue such as liver or kidney but if the tissue contains connective tissue or muscle, then alternative means must be found. The alternatives usually involve a mincer or blender. These may be hand operated, in which case the tissue is then further treated in a Potter homogenizer, or motor driven as with the commercially available Waring Blendor. A pressure system has also found favour in recent years in the form of the Chaikoff Press. This involves forcing the material through fine holes under high pressure.

It is seldom possible to apply osmotic effects alone since many cells are not that easily disrupted but where it is possible this is the method of choice. With red blood cells and reticulocytes the cells are merely suspended in distilled water when they burst open. Sometimes this process is assisted by the addition of a small amount of detergent. Another type of free growing cell is the tumour cell that grows in the ascitic fluid of the abdomen. These cells may also be broken up by osmotic effects. Even though osmotic effects are seldom enough in themselves, they usually play a part in most grinding techniques. Thus the cell membranes will be weakened by changing the osmotic pressure even though the cells do not burst. The structure of the various organelles is also affected by osmotic conditions.

Finally, a technique that has in recent years proved useful is that of ultrasonic vibrations. A suspension of the cells or partially disrupted cells is placed in the field of the vibrations. Although this technique is useful with bacteria and certain animal cells, it is difficult to control. Moreover, very high temperatures are generated at the point of disintegration so that cooling becomes a problem and it is not surprising that many enzymes fail to survive the process.

It will be seen, therefore, that the choice of method for cell disruption is critical and that each problem with each particular tissue must be considered afresh. No method is ideal so that it is necessary to be aware of the snags in each situation.

The Fractionation of Subcellular Particles

Having obtained a suspension that contains whole cells, partially broken cells, nuclei, mitochondria, pieces of endoplasmic reticulum, etc., it is necessary to separate out the various components. In theory this could be achieved by the application of any method that exploited the differences between the physical or chemical properties of the constituents. Thus, for example, electrophoresis has been used, since the electrophoretic mobility of the particles will certainly differ. Unfortunately, the procedure involves electrophoresis without a supporting medium, such as paper, and this presents practical difficulties and means that the quantities that can be handled are very small. Another method is counter-current distribution depending on the surface properties of the particles. Albertsson[7] has shown the potentialities of this method but it has not so far been used very much. Virtually the only method that is routinely used is differential centrifugation and as a result of recent developments the lead of this method over all others has in fact been increased.

The use of differential centrifugation for fractionating particles from, for example, the liver cell, is shown diagrammatically in Fig. 1.2. The rate of sedimentation of a particle in a centrifugal field will depend both on its density and its shape. The figure shows that by centrifuging the suspension at a low force, quoted as g, the nuclei and pieces of partially disrupted tissue are precipitated. If the part that is left in suspension (the supernatant) is then centrifuged again, another fraction is precipitated, and so on. Such fractions are not homogeneous and in fact could not be so even if all the subcellular constituents had markedly different densities. The reason for this is shown in Fig. 1.3[8] and is because the particles are distributed uniformly through the length of the tube at the outset, the first material pelleted being contaminated by all other particle species and by the soluble or non-sedimenting material present. As small particle species are in turn sedimented, these also are contaminated by still smaller or more slowly sedimenting entities to a degree which is roughly proportional to the ratio of their sedimentation rates. The only particles in a multicomponent mixture which may be

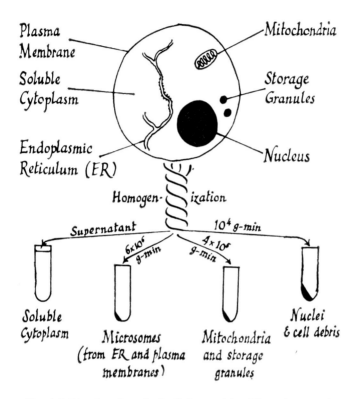

FIG. 1.2. Fractionation of subcellular particles. The units quoted as g-min represent the centrifugal force g multiplied by the number of minutes the material is submitted to this force. (Drawing reproduced by courtesy of V. P. Whittaker.)

obtained in a pure state in a single centrifugation are the last particles sedimented and only part of these. Thus, while by this method it is possible to effect a considerable purification of each of the components of the cell, this requires repeated sedimentation. There are other complications such as those that arise because the particles collide with the walls but we will not consider these.

An alternative method of proceeding is to arrange for the particles to sediment from a thin starting zone into a supporting medium which allows each particle to migrate a distance proportional to the particle sedimentation rate. In practice the supporting medium consists of liquid with a gradient that increases from the top of the tube to the bottom. This procedure is shown in Fig. 1.4. This is known as density gradient centrifugation and is used very extensively at the present time. After centrifugation the components are recovered either by siphoning off the liquid from the bottom of the tube or by puncturing the tube with a needle and collecting drops. We shall be discussing various applications of this technique in later chapters.

It is not necessary to discuss now the nature of the constituents of the different fractions isolated by centrifugation but a few general points should be made. Firstly, it is wrong to assume that because a morphological constituent of one tissue sediments in a certain way, a similar component from another tissue will behave in the same manner. Thus in rat liver, most of the rough endoplasmic reticulum will end up in the so-called "microsome" fraction as shown in Fig. 1.2 but in a tissue such as the hen's oviduct most of the rough endoplasmic reticulum is in the nuclear fraction. The term microsome fraction should, therefore, be confined to express a fraction with certain centrifugal properties; the nature of the morphological constituents contained in the microsome fraction depending on the tissue of origin.

Secondly, because, for example, most of the rough endoplasmic reticulum from rat liver will be present in the microsome fraction this does not mean that some of it will not be found in other fractions. Thus the mitochondrial fraction contains many components other than mitochondria. It follows that it is not possible to claim that an enzyme or antigen is "mitochondrial" unless the fraction in which it has been demonstrated is clearly homogeneous with respect to mitochondria. As we have seen, the reasons for this difficulty are both inherent in the centrifugal methods used and because the cell is not completely disrupted. Furthermore, there is no reason why some of the ribosomes should not be tightly bound to the mitochondria.

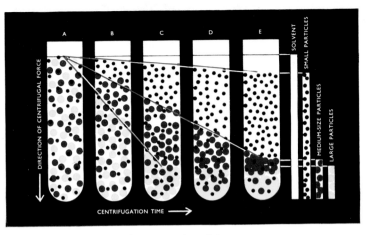

Fɪɢ. 1.3. Diagrammatic presentation of the sedimentation of particles in a swinging bucket centrifuge tube. The distribution of particles is shown in tube *A*. Tubes *B* to *E* show the sedimentation of particles during centrifugation and illustrate the sources of cross-contamination. The sedimentation rates of particle boundaries are indicated by the angled lines. The bars at the right indicate the distribution of solvent and particles in tube *E*.

(Figs. 1.3 and 1.4 are from *Fractions*, see ref. 8.)

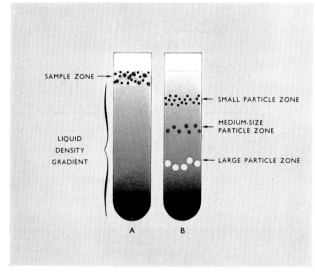

Fɪɢ. 1.4. Rate-zonal centrifugation in a conventional swinging bucket centrifuge tube. Initially, a thin sample zone is layered over a liquid density gradient *A* with the tube at rest. After centrifugation *B* particles having different sedimentation rates are separated into zones at different density levels in the gradient.

References

1. O. GREENGARD, A. SENTENAC and G. ACS, Induced formation of phosphoprotein in tissues of cockerels *in vivo* and *in vitro*, *J. biol. Chem.*, **240**, 1687–91 (1965).
2. C. BRUNI and K. R. PORTER, The fine structure of the parenchymal cell of the normal rat liver, *Amer. J. Path.*, **46**, 691–755 (1965).
3. V. P. WHITTAKER, The application of subcellular fractionation techniques to the study of brain function, *Progr. Biophys. molec. Biol.*, **15**, 39–96 (1965).
4. G. E. PALADE, A small particulate component of the cytoplasm, *J. biophys. biochem. Cytol.*, **1**, 59–68 (1955).
5. S. J. HOLT and R. M. HICKS, The localisation of acid phosphatase in rat liver cells as revealed by combined cytochemical staining and electron microscopy, *J. Cell Biol.* **11**, 47–66 (1961).
6. G. B. PIERCE, jun., J. SRI RAM and A. R. MIDGLEY, jun., The use of labelled antibodies in ultrastructural studies, *Int. Rev. exp. Path.*, **3**, 1–32 (1964).
7. P. A. ALBERTSSON, *Partition of Cell Particles and Macromolecules*, Wiley, New York, 1960; P. A. ALBERTSSON, Partition of double-stranded and single-stranded deoxyribonucleic acid, *Arch. Biochem.*, Suppl. 1, 264 (1962).
8. N. G. ANDERSON, Zonal centrifugation, *Fractions*, **1**, 2–12 (1965) (publ. by Beckman Instruments Inc., Calif.).

Further Reading

A. G. LOEWY and P. SIEKEVITZ, *Cell Structure and Function*, Holt Rinehart & Winston, New York, 1963.

The Liver, Morphology, Biochemistry, Physiology (Ed. C. ROUILLER), 2 vols., Academic Press, London, 1963, 1964.

The living cell, *Scientific American*, September 1961.

G. E. PALADE, The organization of living matter, *Proc. nat. Acad. Sci. Wash.*, **52**, 613–34 (1964).

The Cell (Eds. J. BRACHET and A. E. MIRSKY), 5 vols., Academic Press, New York, 1961.

R. C. NAIRN, *Fluorescent Protein Tracing*, Livingstone, Edinburgh, 1962.

J. PAUL, *Cell Biology*, Heinemann, London, 1965.

Methods of separation of subcellular structural components, *Biochem. Soc. Symp.*, **23** (1963).

S. J. HOLT and R. M. HICKS, Combination of cytochemical staining methods for enzyme localization with electron microscopy, *Symposia for the International Society for Cell Biology*, Ed. by R. J. C. HARRIS, Vol. I, Academic Press, 1962.

S. J. HOLT and R. M. HICKS, Specific staining methods for enzyme localization at the sub-cellular level, *British Medical Bulletin*, **18**, 214–19 (1962).

CHAPTER 2

Mitochondria

Occurrence and General Characteristics

THE largest of the particles which may be isolated from the cytoplasm of virtually all animal cells are the mitochondria. The word "mitochondrion" means "thread-like grain" and this is what the structures look like in the light microscope. As seen *in situ* in cells with the electron microscope, all mitochondria irrespective of source have the same basic structure and biochemists have shown that isolated mitochondria from a variety of cell types in different species also have chemical systems in common. As we have previously stated mitochondria may be thought of as the power house of the cell, but as we shall see their functions are even more embracing than the supply of energy.

An electron micrograph of a portion of a mitochondrion in a rat liver cell is shown in Plate II.1. This shows the common pattern of organization that characterizes mitochondria from different types of cell. The pattern is shown diagrammatically in Fig. 2.1.

The mitochondrion possesses an almost structureless matrix bounded by two membranes. The inner of these is periodically invaginated to form highly characteristic infoldings to which Palade gave the name "cristae mitochondriales". The space enclosed by these infoldings (the intracristal space) is often seen to communicate with the spaces bounded by the inner and outer membranes where the latter run parallel; and together these spaces constitute the external compartment. The fact that in some sections some cristae are not seen to communicate with the external compartment is probably because their orifices do not lie in the plane of sectioning. The two membranes of the mitochondrion are "unit" membranes.

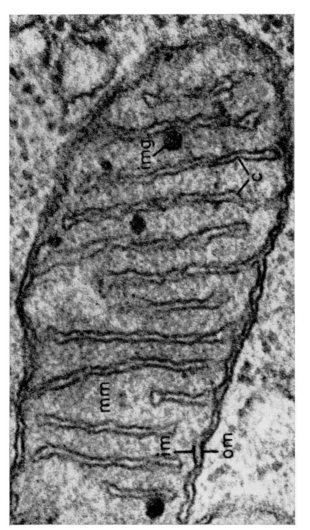

PLATE II.1. Electron micrograph of a section through part of a mitochondrion (pancreatic exocrine cell, guinea-pig). *om*, outer membrane; *im*, inner membrane; *c*, crista; *mm*, mitochondrial matrix (inner chamber); *img*, intramitochondrial granule. Magnification × 100,000. [From G. E. Palade, *Proc. nat. Acad. Sci. Wash.*, **52**, 613 (1964).]

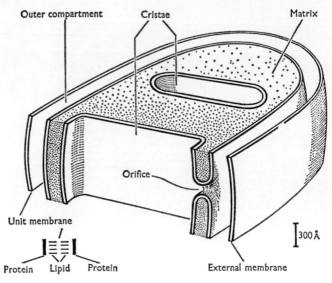

FIG. 2.1. Diagram illustrating the main features of mitochondrial structure as revealed by positive staining and thin sectioning. [From V. P. Whittaker, *Biochem. Soc. Symp.*, **23**, 109 (1963).]

As indicated in Fig. 2.1 such membranes consist of a lipid bilayer with outwardly directed polar groups to which stabilizing layers of glycoproteins are fixed. Thus the external compartment is bounded by hydrophilic surfaces and is unlikely to be filled with lipid.

The function of the infolding of the inner membrane is probably to provide access to the respiratory enzymes and possibly also to provide additional membrane surfaces to accommodate these. The matrix of the mitochondria of cells with a high oxygen uptake, such as those of the flight muscles of insects, is almost entirely occupied by tightly packed, highly ordered cristae and circulation within the cristae is improved by fenestrations.[1]

Conventional electron microscopy reveals only one organelle within the matrix, the dark granules. This is because the light atoms making up biological membranes do not in general scatter electrons sufficiently well to provide adequate contrast for electron microscopy.

In the conventional methods contrast is enhanced by allowing the membrane to react with heavy atoms such as osmium, manganese or lead. More recently an alternative method has been developed, that of negative staining in which the biological membranes are immersed in a pool of electron dense material, such as sodium phosphotungstate, which dries to form an electron dense glass. Membranes now appear as regions of electron transparency against a dark background. The specimen is not sectioned and must be particulate or in the form of a thin film if the negative stain is to penetrate adequately. This method has proved very helpful in determining the structure of mitochondria although a difficulty does arise due to their osmotic sensitivity. All negative stains so far used are strongly hypotonic, any osmotically active substance added to make them isotonic prevents the uniform deposition of negative stain on drying. Some kind of fixation procedure must, therefore, be applied if disruption is to be prevented, although a little disruption may be helpful if it permits the penetration of the negative stain into regions otherwise inaccessible. The fixative found most useful by Whittaker[2] and his colleagues for a variety of mitochondria consists of aqueous neutralized formaldehyde containing osmium tetroxide. Plate II.2 shows a mitochondrion from brain treated in this way. The negative stain will be seen to have penetrated into the external compartment and into the clefts of the matrix which constitute the cristae. The external membrane is clearly visible at a number of points. The negative stain, although it readily penetrates the external membrane of fixed mitochondria filling the external compartment, fails to penetrate into the matrix for reasons which are not yet clear.

The image of the mitochondrion obtained with fixed and negatively stained preparations is fully consistent with the Palade–Robertson concept of mitochondrial structure summarized in Fig. 2.1. The distribution of negative stain confirms that the external compartment is hydrophilic and suggests that the matrix is not simply another aqueous compartment.

Although negative staining cannot be applied to undisrupted tissue, mitochondria can be seen, under favourable circumstances, in

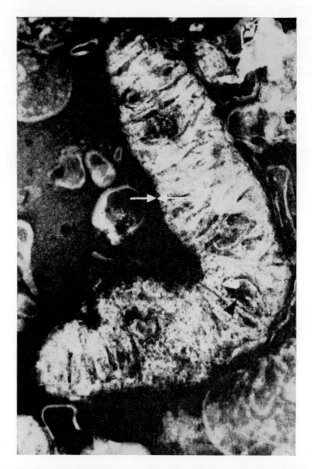

PLATE II.2. Brain mitochondrion, fixed with 0·01% osmium tetroxide and negatively stained with sodium phosphotungstate (pH 7·4). Note external membrane (double arrow), orifices (single arrow) and well-filled external compartment which is seen to penetrate into the matrix as narrow clefts identical with the cristae of the classical structure. (Electron micrograph by courtesy of V. P. Whittaker, A.R.C. Institute of Animal Physiology, Cambridge.)

more or less organized tissue fragments. Such electron micrographs of unsectioned material confirm that mitochondria are indeed elongated structures which is not always apparent from thin sections to which conventional methods have been applied.

The apparent shape and size of mitochondria will depend on whether they are examined after isolation from the cell or *in situ* and the speed with which the fixation was achieved. Mitochondria are usually ellipsoid in shape although they may be either rounder or more elongated. Rat liver mitochondria are typical of the middle of the spectrum in size and shape. They are about $3\cdot3\,\mu$ in length and a little less than $1\cdot0\,\mu$ in width. Elongated mitochondria are seen in the exocrine cells of the pancreas where they may reach $10\,\mu$ in length.

In most cases the cristae are transverse to the long axis but in mammalian neurons in the central nervous system, for example, they are often longitudinal and parallel to the long axis. In insect flight muscle within a single mitochondrion the cristae may be transverse, longitudinal or oblique and may branch and anastomose.

As we shall see mitochondria possess the property, when isolated, of swelling and there seems little doubt that the arrangement of the cristae has a bearing on the ability of a mitochondrion to swell. The cristae are also affected by the nutritional state and endocrine balance of an animal. Even between cells it is possible to correlate the relative activity of the mitochondria in terms of oxidative phosphorylation with the abundance of cristae.

Dynamics

Although electron microscopy has been very useful in revealing the structure of mitochondria this method can tell us little about the variation in shape which an individual specimen can assume. The light microscope is useful here for observing such changes in living cells, particularly phase contrast microscopy and time-lapse cinematography. Frederic[3] has shown that individual mitochondria in a fibroblast change markedly and that various agents such as 2,4-dinitrophenol cause pronounced changes in form. Mitochondria

C

in some cells such as fibroblasts and liver cells are relatively mobile and can move about in the cytoplasm. Under these circumstances they are very plastic. In contrast the mitochondria of skeletal muscle cells are fixed and do not tend to undergo changes in form or volume.

Number per Cell

The number of mitochondria per cell varies enormously. Table 2.1 gives some figures by Lehninger.

TABLE 2.1

Cell type	No.
Sperm cells	24
Renal tubule	300
Liver	800
Sea urchin egg	14,000
Giant amoeba	500,000

Smith[4] has shown that there is a quantitative relationship between total body weight, mitochondrial mass and oxygen utilization in a series of mammals. In rat liver cells the mitochondria contain 15–23% of the total nitrogen of the cell, 18% of the total volume of the cell and 22% of the total cytoplasmic volume as shown in Chapter 1.

FIG. 2.2. The generation of ATP through the oxidation of glucose by the glycolytic and the tricarboxylic acid cycles. From 1 mole of glucose 38 moles of ATP are generated from ADP. *The shaded lower part indicates that there are two flavoprotein enzymes one being specific for succinate. NAD = nicotinamide-adenine-dinucleotide. FP = flavoprotein enzyme, B, C, A, A_3 = cytochromes.

$$1 \text{ glucose} \rightarrow 2 \text{ pyruvate} + 2 \text{ NADH} + 2 \text{ ATP}$$
$$2 \text{ pyruvate} \rightarrow CO_2 + \text{acetylCoA} + 6 \text{ ATP}$$
$$2 \text{ NADH} \rightarrow 2 \text{ NAD}^+ + 6 \text{ ATP}$$
$$2 \text{ acetylCoA} \rightarrow 24 \text{ ATP}$$

$$1 \text{ glucose} \rightarrow 6 \text{ } CO_2 + 6 \text{ } H_2O + 38 \text{ ATP}$$

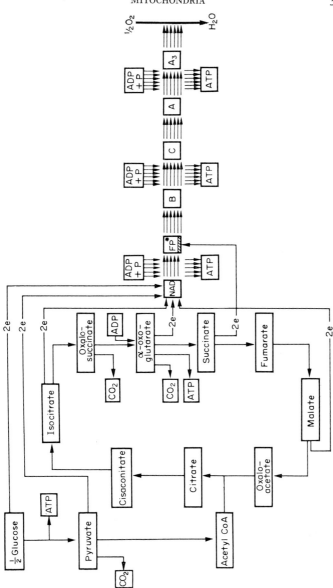

Function

The function of all mitochondria so far studied is the same, namely the release of energy by oxidation of substrates and the conservation of the energy released in the form of the bond energy of ATP. The coupling of oxidation to the synthesis of ATP is the universal function of all mitochondria. Since ATP is the driving force, chemically speaking, for all the key synthetic processes of oxygen requiring organisms, the reason for calling the mitochondrion the power house of the cell should be apparent. The general characteristics of this process will be described.

Figure 2.2 summarizes the reactions which glucose undergoes when it is oxidized to CO_2 and H_2O. The net effect of this oxidation is to produce 38 moles of ATP from ADP for each mole of glucose which is oxidized. The oxidation can be subdivided into three parts. The first is the glycolytic pathway in which 1 mole of glucose is converted to 2 moles of acetyl CoA. This occurs under aerobic conditions and the net result is that 2 moles of ATP are made from ADP and 4H or rather electrons are transferred to NAD. The second part is the tricarboxylic acid or Krebs cycle in which the acetyl CoA is added to oxaloacetate and a series of reactions takes place in which the product is again oxaloacetate. The net result of the operation of one round of this cycle is that six electrons are transferred to NAD and two to another electron carrier, the enzyme flavoprotein containing in its prosthetic groups flavine-adenine-dinucleotide, or FAD. The third part of the oxidation is the so-called electron transport chain in which the electrons accumulated by NAD and the flavoprotein are transferred to the various cytochromes the iron of which is successively oxidized and reduced and ATP is formed from ADP. Finally, the enzyme cytochrome oxidase, called more correctly cytochrome a and a_3, catalyses the transfer of electrons and hydrogen to oxygen to form water.

The enzymes of the glycolytic cycle seem to be located in the soluble part of the cytoplasm but those of the Krebs cycle and the electron transport chain are present in the mitochondria and so are of particular concern to us here. It is necessary at this point to describe some of the outstanding features of the electron transport chain.

P/O ratio

The reason for the large number of steps in the electron transport chain between substrate and oxygen seems to be that it is chemically more efficient to break up the large difference in energy potential into many small steps. At various points along the path the energy latent in the chemical configuration of the substrate is captured and transformed into ATP. Thus the phosphorylation process that accompanies electron transport is the coupling of the phosphorylation by inorganic phosphate of ADP to give ATP. As shown in the diagram for every substrate oxidized via NAD there are three ATP molecules formed for every atom of oxygen that is reduced to form one molecule of water. In the case of succinate the NAD step is by-passed and only two ATP molecules are formed. The oxidation of α-oxoglutarate is different yet again for here one molecule of ATP is formed by direct oxidation of substrate so that in this case four ATP in all are formed. The ratio of moles of inorganic phosphate esterified to form ATP per atom of oxygen consumed during the oxidation is called the P/O ratio.

Coupled phosphorylation

In intact mitochondria the oxidation of substrates necessarily leads to phosphorylation so that electrons are not transported unless ATP is synthesized. This is known, therefore, as coupled phosphorylation. The coupling is so "tight" that under suitable conditions it is reversible so that ATP will drive the process backwards and NAD is reduced to NADH. The coupling can be broken by the use of an agent such as 2,4-dinitrophenol. In the presence of small amounts of this compound oxidation proceeds at a rapid rate but no phosphorylation occurs. Thus 2,4-dinitrophenol is an uncoupling agent. It is presumed that it breaks down the high energy intermediate between the cytochromes and the phosphorylation step.

Active ion translocation

Mitochondria can actively accumulate certain ions from the surrounding medium in a process that is apparently integral with respiratory chain phosphorylation. Active transport may be defined as the movement of specific ions or molecules against a gradient of concentration that is directly dependent on some biological source of energy, such as an ATP supply.

If normal mitochondria are exposed to hypotonic solutions, to detergents or to swelling agents such as phosphate, or incubated at $37°$ in the absence of respiratory substrates, essentially all the K^+ ions and Na^+ ions and about half of the Mg^{2+} ions and Ca^{2+} ions leak into the medium. However, in the presence of respiratory substrate, adenine nucleotide, Mg^{2+} ions and O_2, that is conditions in which oxidative phosphorylation can take place, the concentration of K^+ or Na^+ ions of intact mitochondria can be maintained constant even if the concentration in the medium is considerably lower. It is not clear whether the maintenance of K^+ ion concentration has a stoicheiometric relationship to electron transport. Greater success has attended experiments on the uptake of Ca^{2+} ions.

The uptake of Ca^{2+} ions by mitochondria may be very dramatic so that there may be a fiftyfold increase in Ca^{2+} content of rat kidney mitochondria during respiration *in vitro* in a medium containing Ca^{2+} ions.[5] The uptake of Ca^{2+} ions requires respiration and the presence of inorganic phosphate, ATP, and Mg^{2+} ions. Rossi and his colleagues[6] have shown that inorganic phosphate of the suspending medium accompanies Ca^{2+} ion during their active accumulation. Electron micrographs of such Ca^{2+} loaded mitochondria showed them to consist of two distinct types.[7] By far the largest type contained many large, dense granules in the matrix, while the other type was relatively free of such granules. The two types of mitochondria could be separated by sucrose density gradient centrifugation, those containing the dense granules being the heaviest. The accumulation of calcium phosphate in mitochondria apparently occurs at the so-called dense granules.

Rossi and Lehninger[8] have studied the relationship between Ca^{2+} ion accumulation, inorganic phosphate accumulation and oxygen uptake. The uptake of Ca^{2+} ions is a relatively rapid and massive process and it is probable that there is a quantitative and stoicheiometric relationship between electron transport and ion accumulation. Furthermore, there is also an apparent relationship between Ca^{2+} ion accumulation and the number of phosphorylation sites in the respiratory chain. Green has studied the uptake of Mg^{2+} ions and Chappell that of Mn^{2+} ions.

The physiological significance of active ion accumulation by mitochondria is not at present clear. However, it may be noted that mitochondria make up some 20% of the volume of the liver cell so that they could provide a large ion-sequestering capacity, particularly for Ca^{2+} ions.

Energy conservation

The enzymic and chemical mechanisms of energy conservation in the respiratory chain culminating in the formation of ATP are still unsolved. Most of the postulated mechanisms are based on the principle of a common intermediate in electron transport and in ATP formation. It is assumed that the mechanism is essentially identical at all these phosphorylation sites since they all seem to have the same properties.

Slater[9] has pointed out that most of the postulated mechanisms can be classified into two kinds, type I and type II. Type I mechanisms propose that some substance, not inorganic phosphate, combines with the electron carrier during the coupled oxido-reduction to form a high-energy intermediate. This intermediate is common to the oxido-reduction and the ATP-forming reactions. Inorganic phosphate does not react directly with the electron carrier molecules. In type II mechanism inorganic phosphate is postulated as combining directly with the electron carrier molecule either before or during oxido-reduction. In general the evidence is in favour of type I reaction.

Mitchell[10] has suggested an alternative chemiosmotic mechanism which does not involve a high energy intermediate. In this it is proposed that electron transport along the respiratory chains in the mitochondrial membrane bring about separation of H^+ and OH^- ions across the membrane. It is suggested that the mitochondrial membrane is impermeable to H^+ and OH^- so that electron transport "drives" a pH gradient across the membrane. Mitchell proposes that the pools of H^+ and OH^- so formed in the two aqueous phases separated by the membrane are used to "pull" the formation of ATP from ADP and phosphate by the reverse action of an anisotropic ATPase in the membrane. It is seen that in this proposal the coupling is not a classical one but a physical one made possible by specific penetration of enzymic molecules in a membrane impermeable to H^+ and OH^-.

Specific inhibitors

It may be helpful to briefly consider the effects of the specific inhibitors of mitochondrial metabolism that have played so important a part in unravelling the patterns and mechanisms of respiratory chain phosphorylation. The inhibitors may be divided into three groups.

(a) *Inhibitors of electron transport.* These probably combine with one or another of the electron carriers themselves and not with the enzymes concerned in energy coupling. Examples are HCN, Amytal, Antimycin A, BAL, 2-heptyl 4-hydroxy quinoline *N*-oxide and rotenone.

(b) *Uncoupling agents.* These cause inhibition of the phosphorylation of ADP without affecting the rate of electron transport. The true uncoupling agents act by causing the discharge on breakdown of some high-energy intermediate to regenerate the free carrier and any other components required for continuous respiration. Examples are 2,4-dinitrophenol, nitro- and halophenols, the anti-vitamin K agent dicumarol, the polypeptide antibiotics gramicidin D and tyrocidine, long chain fatty acids and arsenate.

(c) *Inhibitors of phosphorylating oxidation.* These inhibit phosphorylating electron transport in intact mitochondria but do not inhibit non-phosphorylating electron transport as in the Keilin–Hartree particles. Examples are the antibiotics oligomycin, aurovertin and valinomycin, guanidine and some of its derivatives, the glycoside potassium atractylate, the organometallic triethyltin and sodium azide. These compounds are not identical in their action but they all act by combining stoicheiometrically with some intermediate in the coupling sequence to prevent its cycling through the full sequence of electron- and phosphate-transport reactions.

Fatty acid oxidation cycle

In addition to the reactions which we have already described, the mitochondria of several tissues have been found to be capable of oxidizing fatty acids to completion. The reactions involved are shown in Fig. 2.3.

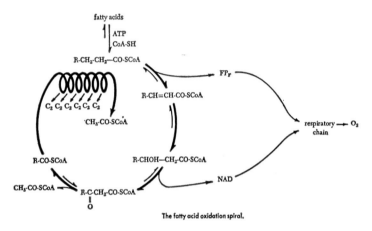

The fatty acid oxidation spiral.

FIG. 2.3. Fatty acid oxidation spiral. (From A. L. Lehninger, *The Mitochondrion*, W. A. Benjamin, Inc., N.Y.)

Three different activating enzymes are known for the formation of the fatty acid CoA esters specific in turn for the short-, inter-mediate- and long-chain fatty acids. They catalyse the general reaction:

$$RCOOH + ATP + CoA \geqq RCOCoA + AMP + PP_i.$$

Ketone body oxidation and formation

In extra-hepatic tissues, such as kidney and heart, isolated mito-chondria readily oxidize β-hydroxybutyrate and acetoacetate via the tricarboxylic acid cycle through the intervention of the following reactions.

$$\beta\text{-hydroxybutyrate} \quad + \quad \begin{cases} \text{NAD} \\ \text{NADH} \end{cases}$$
$$\downarrow$$
$$\text{acetoacetate} + \text{CoA} \quad + \quad \begin{cases} \text{ATP} \\ \text{AMP} \end{cases}$$
$$\downarrow$$
$$\text{acetoacetyl CoA}$$

also acetoacetate + succinyl CoA
→   acetoacetyl CoA
finally acetoacetyl CoA + CoA → Acetyl CoA.

Correlation between Structure and Function

Submitochondrial particles

As we have seen, the intact mitochondrion is a very complex structure so that in order to learn more about its properties biochemists have attempted to disrupt the intact organelle and isolate a smaller fragment which retains at least some of the biological activities of the whole.

Early experiments by Hogeboom and Schneider[11] showed that if mitochondria were treated with ultrasonic vibrations (see Chapter 1) about 55% of the protein was released in soluble form. Presumably the soluble protein was derived from the matrix whereas the easily sedimented insoluble protein represented the membrane. Over 90% of the cytochrome oxidase was thus found to be associated with the membrane.

Many studies in recent years have led to the preparation of submitochondrial particles. Keilin–Hartree particles were obtained by the use of mechanical treatment,[12] those of Cooper and Lehninger by the use of digitonin which yielded membrane fragments[13], and vigorous homogenization was used by Green for the preparation of electron transport particles (ETP).[14] The Keilin–Hartree particles were active in electron transport but not in oxidative phosphorylation, the digitonin particles were capable of both electron transport and oxidative phosphorylation, but at somewhat diminished P/O ratios. The ETP particles were shown by Green and his colleagues to have a fairly complete respiratory chain with the same molar ratios of carrier as in the intact mitochondria. Cytochrome c was not present in such particles for it is easily lost in the extraction procedure. The particles do not catalyse tricarboxylic acid cycle or fatty acid oxidations because most of the enzymes of these cycles are easily extracted in soluble form. It is concluded that such enzymes are either present in the matrix or are only loosely associated with the mitochondria.

The findings of many groups of workers regarding the chemical properties of the various carriers indicate that they are grouped into four as shown in Fig. 2.4.[15] Such complexes have been obtained at least substantially pure and may be recombined to reconstitute the chain.[16]

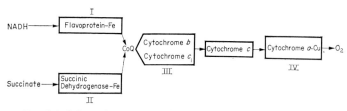

FIG. 2.4. Schematic representation of the four functional primary complexes and their sequential arrangement in the electron-transfer system, in the reconstruction experiments of Hatefi *et al.* (See ref. 16.)

Swelling

Mitochondria change their volume and structure according to their different respiratory states.[17] The organelle swells under the influence of several hormones, the most dramatic effect being caused by the thyroid hormones.[18] In contrast the addition of ATP to the swollen particle causes a contraction but usually not to its former shape.[19] Although this phenomenon of swelling has been much studied its physiological significance is not at present clear.

Fine structure

We have seen that the mitochondrial membrane system not only serves as the structural envelope but also contains the highly organized assemblies of respiratory enzymes that are responsible for the formation of ATP, and for the osmotic work of active transport.

No matter how the mitochondria are disrupted and particles prepared from them nor whether they come from heart mitochondria or liver, they have a very uniform chemical composition. Thus they are composed of 35–60% lipids and 60–65% protein. Over 90% of the lipid is phospholipid, the remainder being tri- and di-glycerides, and cholesterol. It seems probable that the great majority of the lipids serve a purely structural function but some of the components such as the cardiolipin and phosphatidic acid may play a specific role in, for example, the transport of ions.[20]

It has proved very difficult to obtain the mitochondrial proteins in a soluble form and thus enable them to be characterized. The most successful method has been to use a detergent to disperse the membrane such as cholate. It is certain that some proteins form complexes with lipids as has been shown by Criddle, who studied the reaction between cytochrome c and phosphatidyl ethanolamine to form a stable, ether-soluble complex termed lipo-cytochrome c but whether this is the explanation of the tight binding of the proteins to the membranes is not clear. Criddle[16] believes that he has isolated a structural protein from mitochondria that represents 55% of the total membrane protein. He suggests that the membrane is made up of recurring identical protein molecules in a similar manner to the protein coat of viruses.

The electron carriers and coupling enzymes make up 25% or more of the total membrane protein. These components possess the ability to engage in hydrophobic bonding to form insoluble polymers or complexes with each other and with structural protein.

We have previously described the technique of negative staining for electron microscopy and this is certainly proving helpful for correlating the structure and function of fragments isolated from mitochondria. There is evidence that phosphotungstate and other negative stains fix the hydrated structure of lipids.[21] Mitochondria from a number of different tissues, when exposed to negative stain without prior fixation, swell up and burst, extruding large amounts of membranous material in the form of sheets, tubules or ribbons studded with small spherical knobs about 90 Å in diameter. Attention was first drawn to these particles by Fernández–Morán[22] who observed them in negatively stained fragments of mitochondria after they had been treated with ultrasonic vibrations. He and Green suggested that these particles were the ETP particles isolated by Green and his colleagues.[23] Since the above initial finding many groups of workers have seen granule- or particle-studded membranes in association with disrupted mitochondria.[24] An electron micrograph due to Fernández–Morán is seen in Plate II.3. This also shows that the particles are attached to the membranes by stalks.

There seems little doubt that many if not all of the particles are derived from the unpleating of the cristal membrane, the smaller ribbons and vesicles in sonicates being derived by a pinching-off process much as we shall see happens with the endoplasmic reticulum during disruption of the cell.[25] For these reasons the particles are described by some as "inner membrane subunits", but they may not be confined to the inner membrane. Controversy centres on the significance of the particles and it is true that the stalked particles have not been clearly shown as such in undisrupted mitochondria. The present views may by summarized as follows.

Fernández-Morán and Green originally took the view that the head or knob of the stalked particle was a complete respiratory aggregate. It is now accepted that the minimum possible particle weight of such a system (about 10^6) is too large to be accommodated within a 90 Å diameter sphere, which would have a particle weight of only about $2 \cdot 3 \times 10^5$. Lehninger has calculated that the minimum particle weight of the complete respiratory assembly is $1 \cdot 83 \times 10^6$ per cytochrome a monomer and since each assembly probably contains six cytochrome a moieties, the actual particle weight is about $1 \cdot 1 \times 10^7$. Even allowing for various errors it seems that the minimum size of the complete respiratory assembly is about 11 times too large for the theory of Green.

Chance, Parsons and Williams,[26] and Stasny and Crane[27] using rat liver and ox heart mitochondria respectively have stripped the particles off the membrane and found that the membrane still contains cytochromes a, b, and c. This indicates that the particles are not sites of cytochrome activity. Ogawa and Barrnett[28] using a histochemical method found succinate dehydrogenase in the cristal

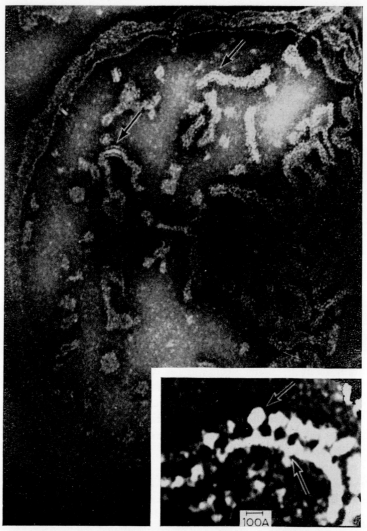

PLATE II.3. Isolated beef heart mitochondrion embedded in thin phosphotungstate layer. Prepared by microdroplet cross-spraying procedure involving only brief interaction of mitochondrial

membranes, the stalked particles, seen only on negative staining, being unreactive.

The view that the particles are formed as the result of disruption, and are therefore artefacts, has received support from the work of Bangham and Horne[21] on artificial lipid mixtures. Thus the addition of lysolecithin to lecithin causes the laminated structure of lecithin to break up into particles of 70–80 Å in diameter, closely resembling the mitochondrial particles. It is conceivable, therefore, that the disruption of mitochondria in hypotonic media is accomplished by the formation of lysolecithin from lecithin followed by the formation of micelles from part of the inner membrane. If, however, stalked particles are an artefact they are an extremely reproducible one and, so far as is known, one which is unique to mitochondrial membranes.

Biogenesis

The origin of mitochondria is a most intriguing problem. The first idea was that they arose *de novo* from other components of the cytoplasm. Against this was the fact that the mitochondria contained many enzymes which were completely absent from the soluble cytoplasm. More recently, it has been shown that even some of those enzymes that do occur in both places are not identical. Thus glutamic-oxaloacetic transaminase which is a component of many mitochondria and is also found in the soluble cytoplasm, has different immunological characteristics when isolated from the two fractions. The enzyme from the mitochondria of different tissues is more

suspension in 0·5 M sucrose with 1% phosphotungstate. Note characteristic paired arrays of elementary particles in profiles of fragmented cristae, which are readily distinguishable from the envelope of the mitochondrion. Magnification × 120,000. Inset is enlarged segment of crista in a specimen similar to above. This shows the three parts of the elementary particle; head piece, stalk, base piece. There is an invariant association of the arrays of head pieces with the underlying dense layer of crista. Note also the segmentation and knob-like protuberance of dense layer at point of attachment of stalk. Magnification × 600,000. [From H. Fernández-Morán, T. Oda, P. V. Blair and D. E. Green, *J. Cell Biol.*, **22**, 63 (1964).]

closely related in structure than the enzyme isolated from the two sites of the same cell.[29]

The cell structures from which mitochondria in the past have been considered to arise are nuclear membrane, plasma membrane and endoplasmic reticulum, but there is no evidence in favour of such suggestions.

The most convincing results favour the idea that mitochondria grow and divide, and for this they would only require biochemical precursors from the rest of the cytoplasm. Luck has studied mitochondria in the mould *Neurospora*.[30] He allowed it to grow in a medium containing radioactive choline until all the lipid was labelled. The cells were then transferred to non-radioactive medium and allowed to grow through the log growth period. Such a culture contains cells in relatively synchronous growth so that the cells could be harvested over three mass-doubling cycles. From the resulting distribution of radioactivity Luck concluded that the mitochondrial mass increases by a continuous addition of new choline-containing lipids and other precursors to existing mitochondria followed by division in a completely random manner.

Bücher[31] and his colleagues have come to a similar conclusion from work on the mitochondria of the locust. During the larval stage of this insect they have followed the acitvity of five typical mitochondrial enzymes and related these to the protein content of the membrane of the mitochondria. They find that there is a remarkably constant relation between the relative activity of the five enzymes and the amount of mitochondrial membrane protein. It seems difficult to accept that this is mere coincidence for if mitochondria were in various stages of assembly from other organelles one would expect to detect differences in the relative amounts of the enzymes present. The similar results from the two different organisms tempts one to conclude that mitochondria do not arise from other organelles and that they are self-reproducing.

If one examines the distribution of mitochondria throughout living cells they are found in all aerobic cells of higher animals and plants as well as in the higher Protists, including algae, protozoa and fungi. In the lower Protists including bacteria and blue–green algae there are no mitochondria. Vanderwinkel and Murray[32] have shown that the respiratory activity in some micro-organisms is localized in the *mesomes*, small vesicular structures with a complex folded membrane system. The respiratory chain enzymes of bacteria are located in the protoplast membrane which appears to have many of the properties of the mitochondrial membrane. In the evolution of higher cells it seems that it became necessary to develop a more complex membrane system for the production of energy. Perhaps it was not sufficient for the energy merely to be generated at the cell membrane since size became too great for surface diffusion to be adequate.

It has been suggested that mitochondria of higher cells may have evolved from micro-organisms that originally parasitized the cytoplasm of a large host cell. The idea would be that such intracellular parasites became non-pathogenic in the course of evolution of the host cell. The bacteria are in many ways similar to mitochondria, being of about the same size, possessing phosphorylating respiratory chains in the membrane, swelling–contraction cycles and ion-transport activities. The major problem would be that the cell membrane of the bacterium would have become permeable to ATP, which it normally is not.

Recently, evidence has been accumulating that mitochondria contain DNA and that this can be used as template in the synthesis of a messenger RNA which guides the formation of protein.[33] (This will be explained more fully in the next chapter.) Nass[34] and his colleagues in Stockholm have shown that fibres with DNA-like characteristics can be demonstrated in mitochondria from a large number of cell types of different species of animals. The idea is that the inherited characteristics of a cell are not entirely controlled by the DNA of the nucleus. This is in accord with the concepts of cytoplasmic inheritance which have been discussed for many years. In the case of mitochondria this would mean that protein would be made which was not identical in structure with the proteins found in other parts of the cell. The evidence already referred to on glutamic-oxaloacetic transaminase is in accord with this idea.

So far as the biosynthesis of various constituents by the mitochondria is concerned, interest has centred mainly on lipids and

46 THE STRUCTURE AND FUNCTION OF ANIMAL CELL COMPONENTS

proteins. The oxidation and biosynthesis of fatty acids is now known to occur by different routes. We have seen that mitochondria oxidize fatty acids but Hülsmann[35] has now shown that they also actively synthesize fatty acids and may in fact be a major site of cellular fatty acid synthesis. Although they can synthesize some phospholipids, it seems that they cannot make the more complex ones.

As to protein synthesis the problem remains rather confused. In the intact animal mitochondrial proteins such as cytochrome *c* are synthesized. Isolated mitochondria undoubtedly incorporate amino acids into protein but this incorporation is not due to the synthesis of cytochrome *c* or other soluble enzymes. Roodyn[36] has obtained evidence that under these circumstances mitochondrial synthesis is concerned with the membrane protein. It may be that such an isolated organelle is in some way defective, or alternatively that the enzymes are synthesized by the endoplasmic reticulum or polysomes associated with the mitochondria and the products passed into the matrix.

References

1. D. S. SMITH, The structure of flight muscle sarcosomes in the blowfly, *J. Cell Biol.*, **19**, 115–38 (1963).
2. V. P. WHITTAKER, The ultrastructure of mitochondria, *Symp. Regulation of Metabolic Processes in Mitochondria*, Bari, Italy, 1966. Elsevier.
3. J. FREDERIC, Recherches Cytoloqique chrondrioma normal, *Arch. Biol. (Liège)*, **69**, 169–342 (1958).
4. R. E. SMITH, Quantitative relations between liver mitochondria metabolism and total body weight in mammals, *Ann. N.Y. Acad. Sci.*, **62**, 403 (1956).
5. F. D. VASINGTON and J. V. MURPHY, Ca^{2+} uptake by rat kidney mitochondria and its dependence on respiration and phosphorylation, *J. biol. Chem.*, **237**, 2670–7 (1962).
6. A. L. LEHNINGER, C. S. ROSSI and J. W. GREENAWALT, Respiration dependent accumulation of inorganic phosphate and Ca^{2+} by rat liver mitochondria, *Biochem. biophys. Res. Comm.*, **10**, 444–8 (1963).
7. J. W. GREENAWALT, C. S. ROSSI and A. L. LEHNINGER, Effect of active accumulation of calcium and phosphate ions on the structure of rat liver mitochondria, *J. Cell Biol.*, **23**, 21–38 (1964).
8. C. S. ROSSI and A. L. LEHNINGER, Stoichiometric relationships between accumulations of ions by mitochondria and the energy-coupling sites in the respiratory chain, *Biochem. Z.*, **338**, 698–713 (1963).

9. E. C. SLATER, Oxidative phosphorylation, *Rev. Pure App. Chem. (Aust)*, **8**, 221 (1958).

10. P. MITCHELL, Coupling of phosphorylation to electron and hydrogen transfer by a chemio-osmotic type of mechanism, *Nature, Lond.*, **191**, 144–8 (1961).

11. G. H. HOGEBOOM and W. C. SCHNEIDER, Cytochemical studies. Physical state of certain respiratory enzymes of mitochondria, *J. biol. Chem.*, **194**, 513–19 (1952).

12. D. KEILIN and E. F. HARTREE, Activity of the succinic dehydrogenase cytochrome system in different tissue preparations, *Biochem. J.*, **44**, 205–18 (1949); K. W. CLELAND and E. C. SLATER, Respiratory granules of heart muscle, *Biochem. J.*, **53**, 547–56 (1953).

13. C. COOPER and A. L. LEHNINGER, Oxidative phosphorylation by an enzyme complex from extracts of mitochondria, *J. biol. Chem.*. **224**, 547–60 (1957).

14. F. L. CRANE, J. L. GLENN and D. E. GREEN, Studies on the electron transport system IV. The electron transport particle, *Biochem. biophys, Acta*, **22**, 475–87 (1956); D. E. GREEN, R. L. LESTER and D. M. ZIEGLER, Studies on the mechanism of oxidative phosphorylation. Preparation and properties of a phosphorylating electron transport particle from beef heart mitochondria, *Biochim. biophys. Acta*, **23**, 516–24 (1957); D. E. GREEN, Studies in organized enzyme systems, *Harvey Lectures*, **52**, 177–227 (1956–7).

15. D. E. GREEN, Structure and function of subcellular particles, *Comp. Biochem. Physiol.*, **4**, 81–122 (1962).

16. R. S. CRIDDLE, R. M. BOCK, D. E. GREEN and H. TISDALE, Physical characteristics of protein of the electron transfer system and interpretation of structure of the mitochondrion, *Biochemistry*, **1**, 827–42 (1962); Y. HATEFI, A. G. HAAVIK, L. R. FOWLER and D. E. GRIFFITHS, Studies on the electron transfer system 42. Reconstitution of the electron transfer system, *J. biol. Chem.*, **237**, 2661–9 (1962); L. R. FOWLER and S. H. RICHARDSON, Studies on the electron transfer system I. On the mechanism of reconstitution of the mitochondrial electron transfer system, *J. biol. Chem.*, **238**, 456–63 (1963).

17. J. B. CHAPPELL and G. D. GREVILLE, The influence of the suspending medium on the properties of mitochondria, *Biochem. Soc. Symp.*, **23**, 39–65 (1963).

18. W. V. SHAW, T. J. LANNON and D. F. TAPLEY, The effect of analogues of thyroxine and 2,4-dinitrophenol on the swelling of mitochondria, *Biochim. biophys. Acta*, **36**, 499–504 (1959).

19. P. V. VIGNAIS, P. M. VIGNAIS, C. S. ROSSI and A. L. LEHNINGER, Restoration of ATP-induced contraction of pretreated mitochondria "by contractile protein", *Biochem. biophys. Res. Comm.*, **11**, 307–12 (1963).

20. E. G. BALL and C. D. JOEL, The composition of the mitochondrial membrane in relation to its structure and function, *Intern. Rev. Cytol.*, **13**, 99–133 (1962).

21. A. D. BANGHAM and R. W. HORNE, Negative staining of phospholipids and their structural modification by surface active agents as observed in the electron microscope, *J. molec. Biol.*, **8**, 660–8 (1964).

22. H. FERNÁNDEZ-MORÁN, Cell-membrane ultrastructure. Low-temperature electron microscopy and X-ray diffraction studies of lipoprotein components in lamellar systems, *Circulation*, **26**, 1039–65 (1962).

23. H. FERNÁNDEZ-MORÁN, T. ODA, P. V. BLAIR and D. E. GREEN, A macromolecular repeating unit of mitochondrial structure and function, *J. Cell Biol.*, **22**, 63–100 (1964).

24. R. W. HORNE and V. P. WHITTAKER, The use of the negative staining method for the electron microscopic study of subcellular particles from animal tissue, *Z. Zellforsch.*, **58**, 1–16 (1962); V. P. WHITTAKER, The separation of subcellular structures from brain tissue, *Biochem. Soc. Symp.*, **23**, 109–26 (1963); D. F. PARSONS, Mitochondrial structure. Two types of subunits in negatively stained mitochondrial membranes, *Science*, **140**, 985–7 (1963); W. STOECKENIUS, Some observations on negatively stained mitochondria, *J. Cell Biol.*, **17**, 443–54 (1963).

25. G. D. GREVILLE, E. A. MUNN and D. S. SMITH, Observations on the fragmentation of isolated flight muscle mitochondria, *Proc. roy. Soc.* **B161**, 403–20 (1965).

26 B. CHANCE, D. F. PARSONS and G. R. WILLIAMS, Cytochrome content of mitochondria stripped of inner membrane structure, *Science*, **143**, 136–9 (1964).

27. J. T. STASNY and F. L. CRANE, The effect of sonic oscillation on the structure and function of beef heart mitochondria, *J. Cell. Biol.*, **22**, 49–62 (1964).

28. K. OGAWA and R. J. BARRNETT, Electron histochemical examination of oxidative enzymes and mitochondria, *Nature, Lond.*, **203**, 724–6 (1964).

29. Y. MORINO, H. KAGAMIYAMA and H. WADA, Immunochemical distinction between glutamic-oxaloacetic transaminases from the soluble and mitochondrial fraction of mammalian tissues, *J. biol. Chem.*, **239**, PC 943–4 (1964).

30 D. J. L. LUCK, The influence of precursor pool size on mitochondrial composition in *Neurospora crassa*, *J. Cell Biol.*, **24**, 445–60 (1965); D. J. L. LUCK, Formation of mitochondria in *Neurospora crassa*, *J. Cell Biol.*, **24**, 461–70 (1965).

31. D. PETTE, M. KLINGENBERG and T. BÜCHER, Comparable and specific proportion in the mitochondrial enzyme activity pattern, *Biochem. biophys. Res. Comm.*, **7**, 425–9 (1962).

32. E. VANDERWINKEL and R. G. MURRAY, Organelles intracytoplasmiques bacteriens et sité d'activité oxydo-réductive, *J. Ultrastructure Res.*, **7**, 185–99 (1962).

33. G. F. KALF, Deoxyribonucleic acid in mitochondria and its role in protein synthesis, *Biochemistry*, **3**, 1702–6 (1964); J. A. PARSONS, Mitochondrial incorporation of tritiated thymidine in *Tetrahymena pyriformis*, *J. Cell Biol.*, **25**, 641–6 (1965).

34. M. M. K. NASS, S. NASS and B. A. AFZELIUS. The general occurrence of mitochondrial DNA, *Exp. Cell Res.*, **37**, 516–39 (1965).
35. W. C. HÜLSMANN, Fatty acid synthesis in heart sarcosomes, *Biochim. biophys. Acta*, **58**, 417–29 (1962).
36. D. B. ROODYN, Protein synthesis in mitochondria III, *Biochem. J.*, **85**, 177–89 (1962).

Further Reading

A. L. LEHNINGER, *The Mitochondrion*, W. A. Benjamin, Inc., New York, 1964.

A. L. LEHNINGER, How cells transform energy, *Scientific American*, September 1961.

A. L. LEHNINGER and C. L. WADKINS, Oxidative phosphorylation, *A. Rev. Biochem.*, **31**, 47–78 (1962).

D. E. GRIFFITHS, Oxidative phosphorylation, *Essays in Biochemistry*, **1**, 91–120 (1965).

L. ERNSTER and C. PHEE, Biological oxidations, *A. Rev. Biochem.*, **33**, 729–88 (1964).

H. A. KREBS and H. L. KORNBERG, Energy transformations in living matter, *Ergeb. Physiol.*, **49**, 212 (1957), and monograph by Springer, Berlin, 1957.

E. RACKER, Mechanisms of synthesis of adenosine triphosphate, *Adv. Enzymol.*, **23**, 323–99 (1961).

A. B. NOVIKOFF, Mitochondria (chondriosomes), *The Cell* (Ed. by J. BRACHET and A. E. MIRSKY), Vol. 2, p. 299. Academic Press, New York, 1961.

G. E. PALADE Electron microscopy of cytoplasmic structures, *Enzymes. Units of Biological Structure and Function* (Ed. by O. H. GAEBLER), p. 185. Academic Press, New York, 1956.

CHAPTER 3

Ribosomes and the Endoplasmic Reticulum

IN THIS chapter we are concerned with the membranous components of the cytoplasm together with the small electron dense particles, the ribosomes. The membrane, which in some cells occupies a large proportion of the cytoplasm, forms a highly intricate three-dimensional network. When the membrane is studded with ribosomes it is called rough-surfaced endoplasmic reticulum, and in the absence of ribosomes smooth-surfaced endoplasmic reticulum. Ribosomes may also be present in the cytoplasm in the absence of membrane. We shall see that the ribosomes are concerned with the synthesis of protein and that when they form part of the rough endoplasmic reticulum the membrane plays a role in segregating the proteins that are to be exported from the cell. The smooth endoplasmic reticulum plays no part in protein synthesis but has various other functions. We will, therefore, consider first what we may call the blueprint for protein synthesis in the cell, then the role of ribosomes in protein synthesis, and finally the functions of the smooth endoplasmic reticulum.

Protein Synthesis—General Scheme

The reaction of an amino group of one amino acid with the carboxyl group of another to form a peptide bond requires energy. The energy is, of course, provided by ATP and it is the carboxyl group of the amino acid that is converted to an adenylate in the reaction shown on page 51.[1]

The next step is for the amino acid to be transferred to a special kind of RNA. This was discovered by Hoagland of Boston and shown to be present in the soluble fraction of the cell, that is, it was not associated with any of the particles.[2] Because of this it has come to be called soluble or S-RNA. Other names have been used such as transfer RNA or acceptor RNA but S-RNA will be used here. Most

Adenosinetriphosphate + Amino acid

Pyrophosphate + Amino acid adenylate

kinds of RNA have a very large molecular weight but S-RNA is exceptional in that it is about 29,000 and contains only 80 nucleotides. One particular kind of S-RNA was the substance which provided in the hands of Holley the first complete structure of any nucleic acid.[3]

The reaction involving the transfer of the amino acid to S-RNA is shown in Fig. 3.1. This shows that the type of linkage of the amino acid is changed from that of a mixed anhydride to an ester. Nevertheless, the important point is that the bond strength of the linkage of amino acid to S-RNA is about the same as in a peptide.

There is at least one different kind of S-RNA for each species of amino acid. The enzyme which is specific for the activation of each amino acid is responsible also for catalysing the transfer of the amino acid to its appropriate S-RNA. As already mentioned we now know the sequence of nucleotides in one of the S-RNA molecules and this is the one that is specific for alanine. This is shown in Fig. 3.2. We

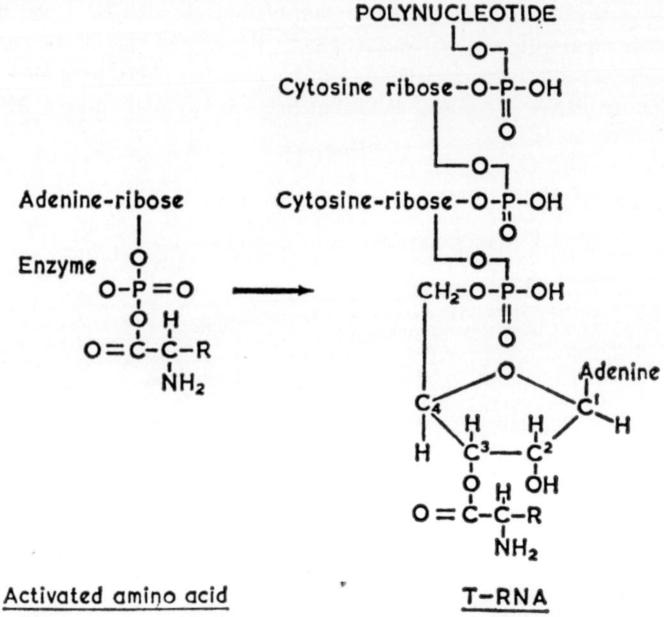

FIG. 3.1. Structural aspects of the transfer of amino acid from amino acid adenylate to S-RNA.

do not yet know the difference in structure between various types of S-RNA. It is certain that in all cases the amino acid is attached to the ribose of adenosine and that the next two nucleotides in the chain contain cytidine, and so any differences must occur elsewhere in the chain.

As will be explained in detail in Chapter 4 we believe that it is the sequence of the four bases that occur in the nucleotides of DNA in the nucleus that determines the sequence of the amino acids that are built into the protein synthesized in the cytoplasm. The blueprint for the translation of this information is shown in Fig. 3.3. This shows that a special kind of RNA, known as messenger RNA (m-RNA) is made using the DNA of the nucleus as a template. Hence the sequence of bases in the nucleotides of the m-RNA reflects the sequence in DNA. The m-RNA then associates with the

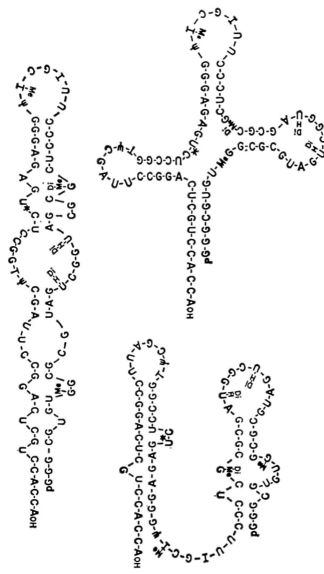

FIG. 3.2. Schematic representation of three conformations of the alanine S-RNA with short, double-stranded regions. (From R. W. Holley et al., ref. 3.)

(Copyright 1965 by the American Association for the Advancement of Science.)

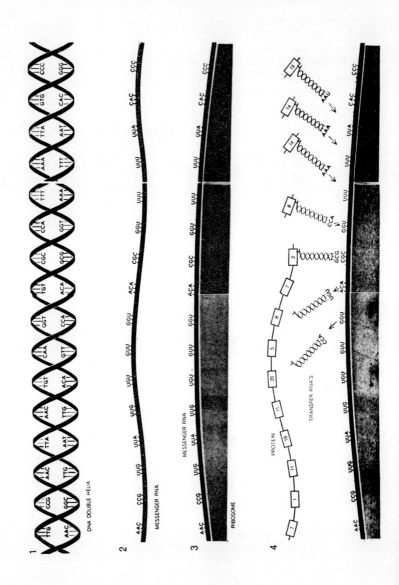

ribosome as shown and it is here that the amino acids attached to their respective S-RNAs are assembled into a peptide chain.

The reason that the bases in the figure are grouped into triplets is that there are only four different kinds of bases in the nucleic acids and twenty different amino acids in the proteins. Hence one base cannot "code" for one amino acid and the minimum number of four different bases that theoretically could code for one of twenty amino acids is three. We now know from some recent experiments of Nirenberg[4] that this is in fact the case. Hence the correct S-RNA must locate itself alongside the correct triplet on the m-RNA and the only way we can visualize this is for a triplet of bases on the S-RNA to base pair with the triplet on the m-RNA (the idea of base pairing will be explained in Chapter 4). Since we do not know the structure of more than one S-RNA we do not know the whereabouts of the critical triplet on the S-RNA.

When the S-RNA with amino acid attached has aligned itself alongside the growing peptide chain an exchange takes place with the release of free S-RNA. This reaction although perfectly feasible is not yet precisely understood. It is clear that additional energy is required and that guanosine triphosphate (GTP), not ATP, is utilized. Also it is known that two different enzymes, known as transferases, are involved.[5]

The idea of m-RNA carrying the information from the DNA of the nucleus to the ribosome in the cytoplasm was worked out by a group led by Brenner, Meselson and Jacob[6] working from kinetic results on phage infected *Escherichia coli*. The idea was clinched about a year later by Nirenberg and Matthaei[7] who showed that the

---

FIG. 3.3. General scheme of protein synthesis. The process begins with the genetic code embodied in DNA (1). The code is transcribed into messenger RNA (2). The messenger RNA finds its way to the ribosome (3). Amino acids indicated by numbered rectangles, are carried to proper sites on the messenger RNA by molecules of S-RNA. The bases are actually equidistant and not grouped in triplets and the mechanism of recognition between S-RNA and messenger RNA is hypothetical. Linkage of amino acid subunits creates a protein molecule. (From M. Nirenberg, *Scientific American*, March 1963.)

nature of the polypeptide synthesized by ribosomes from *E. coli* could be influenced by the presence of a polynucleotide. Thus when a synthetic polynucleotide containing only uridylic acid (poly U) was present in the incubation medium the ribosomes made only polyphenylalanine. This was the first clear cut demonstration of a reaction involving m-RNA. After that a whole variety of synthetic polynucleotides were tried and the connection between the composition of the nucleotide and that of the resulting polypeptide was determined. In this way one or more triplets were assigned to each of the twenty different amino acids.[8] We shall have occasion later to refer to the use of these synthetic m-RNA.

Structure of Ribosomes

We must now summarize what is known of the structure of ribosomes from animal cells. Unfortunately, the situation with the latter is not as clear as it is when ribosomes from bacteria are considered so that we must make comparisons wherever it is helpful.

All the ribosomes that have been isolated from animal cells have a sedimentation constant in the ultracentrifuge of 75–85S. This compares with the 70S of bacterial ribosomes. Animal ribosomes consist of approximately equal amounts of RNA and protein whereas in bacteria the proportion is two-thirds RNA and one-third protein.

If a preparation of ribosomes is treated with a low concentration of Mg^{2+} ions (2.5×10^{-4} M) and is then examined in the ultracentrifuge two peaks instead of one are present. The sedimentation constants of the two peaks from the 70S ribosomes of bacteria are 50S and 30S respectively which in terms of molecular weight means 1.2 and 0.6 million so that the larger unit is twice the size of the smaller. For ribosomes from animal cells three peaks are usually seen with sedimentation constants in the ranges, 62–65S, 45–60S and 27–40S. One can speculate that these peaks also arise from the breakdown of the 80S ribosome to subunits of about 32 and 52S but the position is less clear than with bacterial ribosomes. Petermann states that in the best preparation from the Jensen rat sarcoma the ratio of size between the units is 2.7.

The idea that a ribosome consists of two subunits is also supported by electron microscopy. Huxley and Zubay[9] used negative staining with phosphotungstic acid to examine the ribosomes from *E. coli* and Plate III.1 shows the results. The two subunits differ in stability, the smaller one being less stable. When latent ribonuclease is present in ribosomes then this appears to be associated with the 30S and not the 50S subunit.[10]

We have stated that the ribosomes consist of protein and RNA. About the protein there is little to be said at present. It seems to consist of subunits of about 25,000 molecular weight but whether all the subunits are identical or whether they consist of some twelve different types is disputed. Concerning the RNA much more is known and it may be extracted in various ways. The RNA from the intact ribosome yields two peaks in the centrifuge of 28S and 16S, the 28S being derived from the large subunit and the 16S from the smaller. The base composition of the two RNAs is usually very similar so that one may be a dimer of the other. Spirin[11], in Moscow, has made some proposals as to the way in which the RNA and protein is disposed in the ribosome subunits based on a detailed electron microscopical study using negative staining but the results are no more than tentative. There is, as yet, no clear cut separate biological role which can be assigned specifically to the RNA or the protein.

Ribosome Subunits and Protein Synthesis

Having described what is known of the structure of the ribosome and its subunits we must now see how they fit together at the site of peptide bond formation. Gilbert[12] has made a close study with ribosomes from *E. coli*. He showed first that for protein synthesis to occur the intact 70S ribosome was required, i.e. both the 30S and 50S subunit. The S-RNA was bound only to the 50S subunit and for this to occur the terminal nucleotides at the end to which the amino acid is attached had to be intact. He concluded that the point of binding of S-RNA was near the site at which the amino acid was attached and from which the polypeptide chain grew.

By using poly U as m-RNA Takanami concluded that the m-RNA was bound to the 30S subunit. There is now ample evidence in

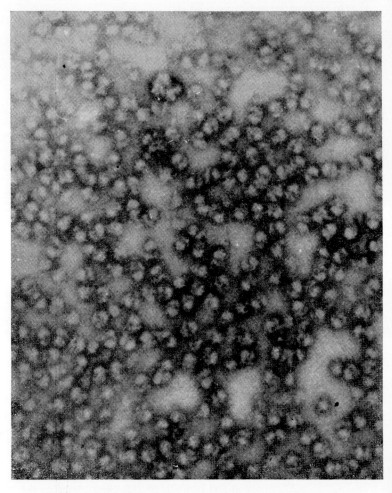

PLATE III.1. Electron micrograph of ribosomes from *E. coli*. The particles were negatively stained with phosphotungstic acid. Most of the particles show two unequal subunits. Magnification × 200,000. (Electron micrograph by courtesy of H. E. Huxley, Lab. of Molecular Biology, Cambridge.)

support of these ideas both from bacterial and animal ribosomes. The situation can, therefore, be shown in diagrammatic form in Fig. 3.4. There are now reports that two molecules of S-RNA are attached to the ribosome at any one time but that only one carries the polypeptide chain, the other merely bringing in the new amino acid.[13] Reference to Fig. 3.3 will show that this is a reasonable expectation.

Polyribosomes

At the end of 1962 a report was published which showed that in reticulocytes the active units were not the individual ribosomes but a group of these units. The work on reticulocytes was done mainly by Warner, Rich and Hall in Boston.[14] Their evidence was based both on electron microscopy and analysis in the ultracentrifuge. A typical electron micrograph of an isolated fraction containing reticulocyte polysomes is shown in Plate III.2. In the case of haemoglobin with a chain of 150 amino acids, the most usual number of ribosomes which were linked together was 5. A calculation based on

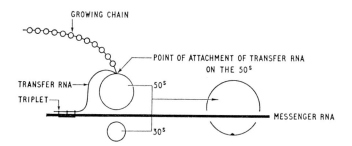

FIG. 3.4. Diagrammatic representation of the relationship between a ribosome, messenger RNA, S-RNA and the polypeptide chain. Messenger RNA is attached to the 30S subunit of the ribosome. The S-RNA is attached at one point to the 50S subunit of the ribosome. This point of attachment is at the same site as that of the growing polypeptide chain. It is postulated that the S-RNA contains a region that base-pairs with the messenger RNA, as indicated in Fig. 3.2. This scheme is based on the work of Gilbert (ref. 12).

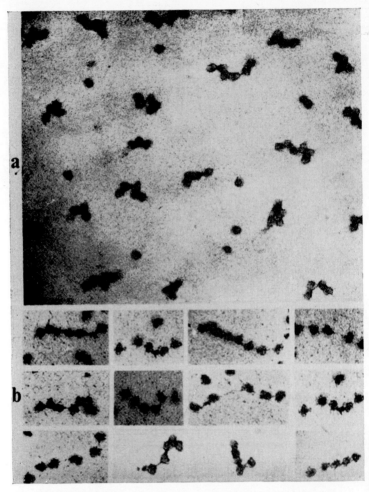

PLATE III.2. Polysomes from rabbit reticulocytes. The polysomes were stained in positive contrast with uranyl acetate. (a) Shows compact fields, where the polysome is a linear array and the ribosomes appear in contact. (b) Shows extended fields, where the polysome is in a linear array, but the ribosomes are often separated by a thin strand. Magnification × 100,000. [From H. S. Slayter, J. R. Warner, A. Rich and C. E. Hall, *J. molec. Biol.*, **7**, 652 (1963).]

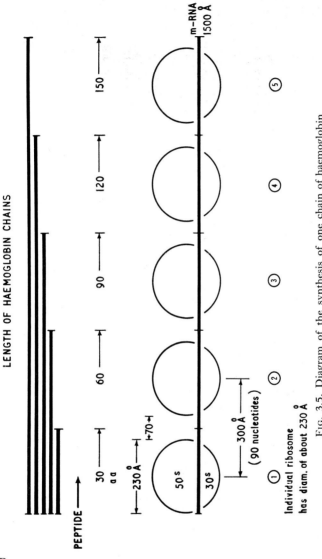

FIG. 3.5. Diagram of the synthesis of one chain of haemoglobin (150 amino acids) by a 5 membered polysome.

D

the idea that each amino acid requires a triplet of nucleotides to code for it shows that a m-RNA of 1500 Å is required. Knowing the approximate size of a ribosome at 230 Å we are left with the satisfying conclusion that there is just room for 5 ribosomes on the strand of m-RNA. The dimensions are shown in Fig. 3.5.

The evidence that the ribosomes are actually linked together by m-RNA is not conclusive. It is based on the hypothesis that a thin thread of m-RNA is more susceptible to the action of ribonuclease than the tightly coiled RNA, complexed with protein, that is present in the ribosomes. If a polysome preparation is treated with a low concentration of ribonuclease at a suboptimal temperature the individual ribosomes are released while the ribosomal RNA appears to be unaffected. This finding, which applies to polysomes irrespective of source, is supporting evidence that the linking strand is composed of RNA.

The concept of the polysome demonstrates in a very neat way how the protein synthetic potential of a necessarily long strand of m-RNA can be economically employed. Thus many ribosome units can function simultaneously. The ribosomes are believed to move along the strand of messenger RNA retaining their polypeptide chains until they reach the end of the strand. The mechanism whereby the completed protein is released is not yet known but this scheme would explain why it is not possible to find partially completed polypeptide chains in cell extracts. The free ribosome released from the end of the strand of m-RNA is available again for addition to the beginning of the strand in the space created by the movement of the ribosomes.[15]

From the experiments with virus infected cells, such as polio infected HeLa cells, it is now apparent that the messenger RNA molecules for a number of different proteins are joined together. Thus in this case one single strand of the m-RNA contains the information for the synthesis of up to ten different proteins.[16] The length of m-RNA that carries the information that determines the sequence of amino acids in a protein is known as a cistron, so that a m-RNA that controls the formation of more than one protein is said to be polycistronic. As has been explained, in a m-RNA with only one cistron the protein is released as the ribosome is detached at the end of the strand. In a polycistronic m-RNA some mechanism must be present for causing the release of one protein and for starting the formation of the next.

The pattern of protein synthesis is summarized in Fig. 3.6.

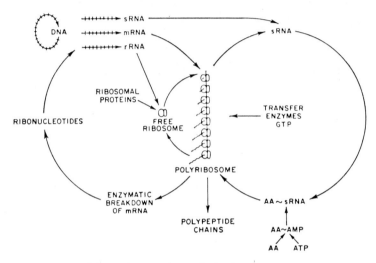

FIG. 3.6. Scheme for protein synthesis. (From J. D. Watson, in *Bull. Soc. Chim. Biol.*, **46**, 1399–1425 (1964).

Experiments with Microsome Fractions

Having described in general terms how we believe that proteins are synthesized we must now examine the evidence for the role of the morphological constituents of the cytoplasm. It is most convenient if we consider first the liver cell.

The assocation between RNA and protein synthesis was suggested 20 years ago by Caspersson,[17] in Stockholm, and Brachet,[18] in Brussels. They showed that tissues that synthesize large amounts of protein are rich in RNA. At about the same time the Belgian cytologist Claude,[19] working then in New York, isolated a fraction from

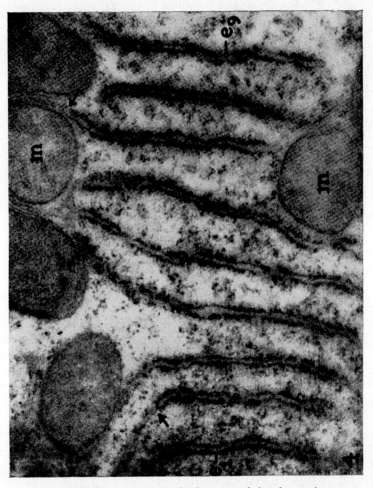

PLATE III.3. Electron micrograph of an array of nine elongated profiles (e_1, e_9) of the rough-surfaced variety and five mitochondrial
profiles (m) in the cytoplasm of a parenchymal rat liver cell. The
elongated profiles are disposed parallel to one another at more or less
regular intervals. In three dimensions the array corresponds to a
pile of vesicles. The outside surface of the membrane limiting these
profiles bears numerous attached particles of small size and high

disrupted liver cells in which the RNA and phospholipid was concentrated and which he named the "microsomes". This fraction was not definitely identified with a morphological constituent until Palade and Siekevitz showed by electron microscopy that the liver microsome fraction contained fragments of the rough-surfaced endoplasmic reticulum.[20] The granules on the membranes were at this time called Palade granules, the term ribosome being coined by Roberts[21] many years later.

Plate III.3 shows a section of the rough endoplasmic reticulum in a rat liver cell at high magnification and Plate III.4 shows a section of the liver microsome fraction. In considering the shape of the fragments of the reticulum seen in such an electron micrograph one has to remember that the membranes come from a complex three-dimensional structure that in the course of preparation for electron microscopy will have been sectioned at many different angles.

Borsook,[22] in California, and Hultin,[23] in Sweden, were the first biochemists to demonstrate the importance of the microsome fraction in protein synthesis. Their observations were developed by Zamecnik and his group in Boston. These workers showed that if a rat was injected with a ^{14}C-labelled amino acid and pieces of the liver removed and subfractionated at various times after injection, the microsome fraction contained the most radioactive protein. The results of a typical experiment are shown in Fig. 3.7. In order to determine the role of the membranous component Zamecnik repeated his previous experiment, but this time treated the microsome pellet with deoxycholate to solubilize the membrane and leave only the granules. He then examined the activity of each fraction. The results, shown in Fig. 3.8, indicated that it is the particles and not the membrane, which are active in protein synthesis. Plate III.5 is an electron micrograph of such particles. It is better to reserve the word ribosome for the particles in the intact cell and to describe

---

density. A few similar particles appear freely scattered in the intervening cytoplasm. The arrows indicate continuity between rough-surfaced and smooth-surfaced profiles. Magnification × 49,000. [From G. E. Palade and P. Siekevitz, *J. biophys. biochem. Cytol.*, **2**, 171 (1956).]

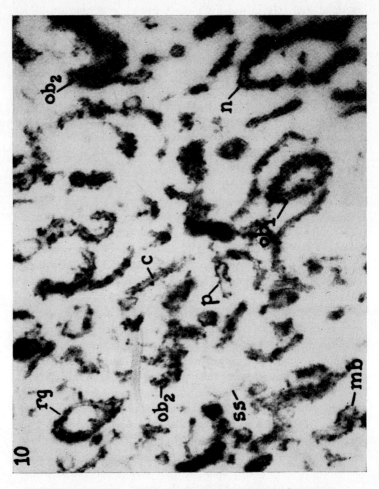

PLATE III.4. Electron micrograph of a microsome pellet from a rat liver homogenate in 0·88 M sucrose. *rg* indicates ring-shaped profiles of the rough endoplasmic reticulum; *n*, a normally sectioned fragment; ob_1 and ob_2, fragments cut at increasing degrees of obliquity; *ss*, smooth surfaced profiles; *mb* is the membrane of the microsomes; *c*, their content; and *p*, attached particles. (Original reference as for Plate III.3.)

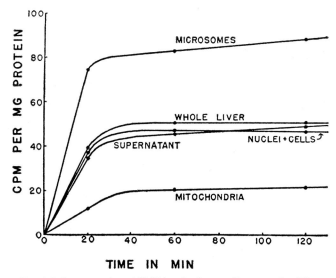

FIG. 3.7. Incorporation of [^{14}C] leucine into rat liver proteins. Time curve for liver fractions *in vivo*. [From E. B. Keller, P. C. Zamecnik and R. B. Loftfield, *J. Histochem. Cytochem.*, **2**, 378 (1956).]

particles that are released from the membrane by deoxycholate as ribonucleoprotein particles since their properties differ from those of the original ribosomes.

The next development was for Zamecnik to demonstrate that when the liver microsome fraction was incubated with a source of ATP and radioactive amino acid the mixture of proteins in the fraction became radioactive.[24] This observation suggested that protein synthesis had taken place. Zamecnik then incubated the ribonucleoprotein particles to see if they synthesized protein but found them to be inactive. Some time later Korner,[25] at Cambridge, repeated this experiment but first carefully washed the particles free of deoxycholate and found that they were now as active for protein synthesis as the original microsome fraction. It is now realized that deoxycholate inhibits protein synthesis.

So far we have been considering the liver cell, in which most of the

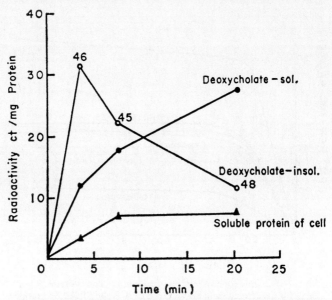

FIG. 3.8. Incorporation of [^{14}C] leucine into the two components of the microsomes and into the soluble protein of the liver cell after intravenous injection of a rat. The per cent RNA by weight of each deoxycholate-insoluble sample is indicated. The per cent RNA averaged 2·1 in the deoxycholate-soluble fraction and 1·7 in the soluble fractions of the cell. [From J. W. Littlefield, E. B. Keller, J. Gross and P. C. Zamecnik, *J. biol. Chem.*, **217**, 111–23 (1955).]

ribosomes are attached to membranes, but, as we have previously stated, some cells such as the reticulocyte, contain very little endoplasmic reticulum. Schweet, then working in California, showed that the microsome fraction from the reticulocytes of rabbits rendered anaemic by the injection of phenylhydrazine was active for protein synthesis. As expected this fraction contained only ribosomes

PLATE III.5. Electron micrograph of ribonucleoprotein particles from rat liver. In the pellet may be seen two kinds of particles (A) and (B). The particles were prepared by the method of R. Rendi and T. Hultin. Magnification × 100,000. *Exp. Cell Res.*, **19**, 253 (1960). (Electron micrograph by courtesy of R. M. Hicks, Bland Sutton Institute of Pathology, The Middlesex Hospital.)

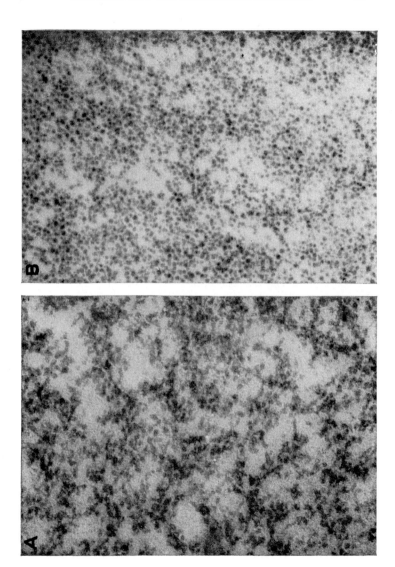

and no membrane. The majority of the protein synthesized by reticulocytes is haemoglobin and Schweet later showed that the isolated ribosomes were also able to synthesize this protein.[26] The reticulocyte and the isolated ribosomes from it have proved to be excellent material for determining the mechanism of synthesis of a specific protein.

Subcellular Components from Liver

As was pointed out in Chapter 1 the liver makes large quantities of protein both for its own purposes, i.e. for the enzymes necessary for it to perform its manifest metabolic reactions, and for export in the form of plasma proteins. Among the plasma proteins, albumin is present in greatest amount, and since it appears to be a homogeneous protein containing only one polypeptide chain, and is fairly easy to isolate in a pure form, its biosynthesis has been studied extensively. It obviously provides a good example of those proteins synthesized by the liver for export.

Both by studies in the intact animal[27] and on isolated fractions[28] it is clear that the microsomes from rat liver are capable of synthesizing serum albumin. The isolated fraction is able to synthesize the complete chain but most of the activity in this case is devoted to the completion of chains which are about half complete on isolation. Such a process is shown diagrammatically in Fig. 3.9.

Although it has been stated previously that fragmented rough endoplasmic reticulum forms the predominant morphological component of the liver microsome fraction, this does not mean that other components are not also present. The microsome fraction in fact contains substantial amounts of smooth surfaced reticulum and so it was interesting to know whether the latter component played a part in protein synthesis. It is possible to separate the rough and smooth reticulum by density gradient centrifugation (see Chapter 1), and Peters has applied such a method to liver after first injecting a rat with [14C] leucine. Since each of the fractions contained approximately equal amounts of albumin he was able to determine the specific radioactivity of the albumin in each fraction at different times

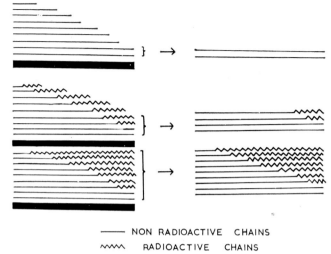

———— NON RADIOACTIVE CHAINS

∿∿∿   RADIOACTIVE CHAINS

FIG. 3.9. Sequential assembly of polypeptide chains. (From J. R. Sargent and P. N. Campbell, ref. 28.)

after injection of radioactive amino acid. Peters' results, which are shown in Fig. 3.10 indicate that the initial site of albumin synthesis is the rough endoplasmic reticulum, the newly synthesized albumin only passing to the smooth reticulum later.

The activity of the smooth reticulum can also be checked by first separating the rough and smooth membranes and then incubating them with ^{14}C-labelled amino acid. For this purpose a method devised by Dallner[29] and his colleagues in Stockholm may be used. The results of such an experiment are shown in Table 3.1. It is seen that while the unfractionated microsome and the rough fractions are quite active the smooth fraction was virtually inactive. If poly U was added to the incubation medium as synthetic m-RNA then all fractions were stimulated but the smooth fraction was affected most. The poly U is not having its effect on the membrane component of the smooth fraction but on the free ribosomes which can be shown by electron microscopy to contaminate it.

From the above experiments it is fair to conclude that in the un-fractionated microsomes in the absence of poly U the active component consists of fragments of the rough endoplasmic reticulum and that the smooth membrane is inactive. The idea that the free

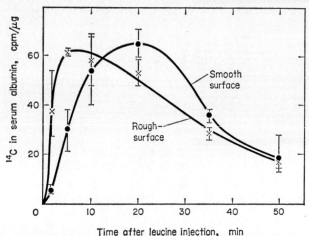

FIG. 3.10 [^{14}C] Leucine incorporation *in vivo* into serum albumin from rough surface and smooth surface microsome fractions. The range of individual values is shown. [From T. Peters, jun., *J. biol. Chem.*, **237**, 1186 (1962).]

TABLE 3.1. EFFECT OF POLY U ON [^{14}C] PHENYLALANINE INCORPORATION BY LIVER MICROSOME SUBFRACTIONS

	Fraction					
	Unfractionated		Rough		Smooth	
Additions	Count	Ratio	Count	Ratio	Count	Ratio
None	922		408		33	
Poly U 25 μg	6122	6·6	3213	7·9	1157	35
50 μg	6752	7·3	4119	10·1	1582	48

Radioactivity as c/min/mg protein
[From P. N. Campbell, C. Cooper and M. Hicks, *Biochem. J.*, **92**, 225 (1964).]

ribosomes are also virtually inactive in the absence of poly U is supported by the work of Hiatt[30] in Boston. He separated the ribosomes bound to membrane from the free ribosomes by sucrose density gradient centrifugation. The method is described in Fig. 3.11 and the results for normal adult rat liver are given in Fig. 3.12. The sedimentation constant of the free ribosomes was, as expected, about

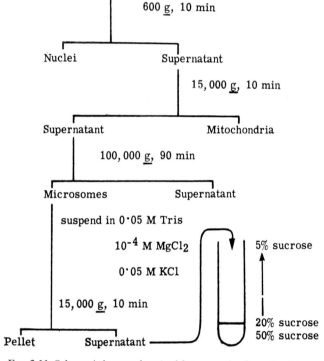

FIG. 3.11. Schematic layout of method for separating bound and free ribosomes in a liver microsome fraction. (Taken from E. C. Henshaw, T. B. Bojarski and H. H. Hiatt, ref. 30.)

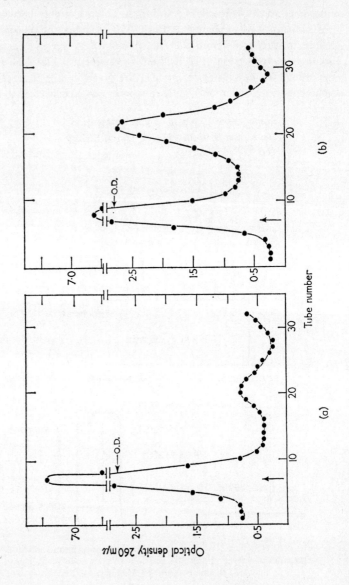

83S. Hiatt studied the activity of the two types of ribosomes after injecting a rat with ^{14}C-labelled amino acid and then isolating the two fractions and determining their activity. He came to the conclusion that the free ribosomes were inactive and that the main activity was in the bound ribosomes.

Hiatt was aware that if polysomes existed that were not attached to membrane they would have a density between that of the bound and free ribosomes but he could find no sign of the presence of such a constituent. When a rat is born its liver has plenty of ribosomes in the cytoplasm but few of these are bound to membranes. However, Oliver,[31] from Perth, Australia, finds that by 5 days after birth a good deal of rough endoplasmic reticulum has been formed and that thereafter the young liver rapidly takes on the appearance of the adult. The appearance of the liver of a rat 5 days after birth is shown in the electron micrograph in Plate III.6. Many of the ribosomes not obviously attached to membrane are in the form of polysomes. If the method of Hiatt is applied to liver from 5-day-old rats, as expected, the proportion of free particles is much greater than in adult liver (see Fig. 3.13). Although there is material between the peaks, there is not much of it as measured by its optical density at 260 mμ. (The absorption at this wavelength is mainly due to RNA.) A subfraction of the microsomes may be prepared that apparently contains only the free ribosomes, and this may be incubated with ^{14}C-labelled amino acid under conditions suitable for protein synthesis. If the incubation mixture is then subjected to the Hiatt procedure and the radioactivity of the protein in each fraction from the gradient is determined, the results shown in Fig. 3.14 are obtained. This experiment shows that the main protein synthesizing activity

Fig. 3.12. Sucrose density gradient centrifugation analysis of the microsomal fraction from rat liver. Tube 1 is from the bottom of the gradient and tube 32 from the top. The tubes contain a gradient of sucrose from 20 to 5% with 50% at the bottom of the tube. The 20–50% sucrose interface is located at about tube 7 (arrow). Centrifugation was for 2½ hr. The rat was starved (a) overnight and (b) for 5 days before the liver was taken. The heavier peak contains ribosomes bound to endoplasmic reticulum and the lighter peak free ribosomes. (From Henshaw et al., ref. 30.)

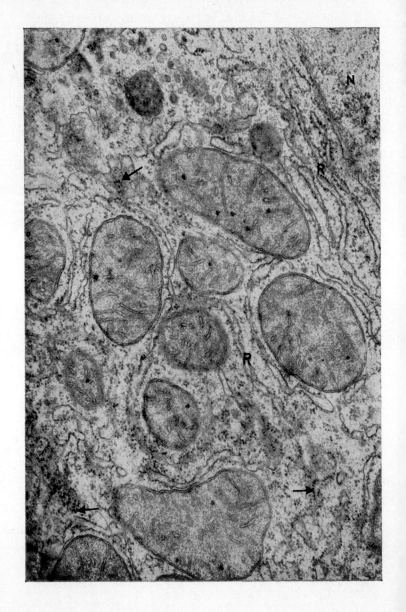

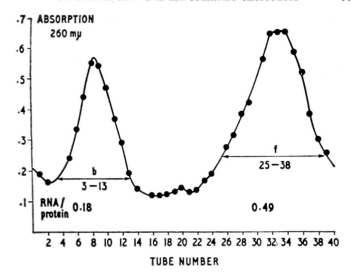

FIG. 3.13. The separation of bound and free ribosomes from the liver of a young rat. The liver was obtained 5 days after birth. Conditions as for Fig. 3.12.

resides in some material that has a higher density than the free ribosomes and that, as expected, the latter are comparatively inactive. When this fraction was treated with a low concentration of ribonuclease after incubation and before gradient centrifugation virtually all the radioactivity had moved to the free ribosome peak. These results are consistent with the idea that free polysomes are active in protein synthesis. The most probable reason for not detecting them in the purely analytical density gradient (e.g. Fig. 3.13) is that they have a broad spectrum of density and are present in the isolated fraction at a comparatively low concentration. The free polysomes

PLATE III.6. Electron micrograph of a parenchymal liver cell from a 5-day-old rat. Many ribosomes are free in the cytoplasm but some are attached to membranes of the endoplasmic reticulum (R). Aggregates of ribosomes in the form of polysomes can be seen in places (arrows). N, nucleus. (Electron micrograph by courtesy of R. M. Hicks). [From P. N. Campbell, G. Serck-Hanssen and E. Lowe, *Biochem. J.*, **97**, 422 (1965).]

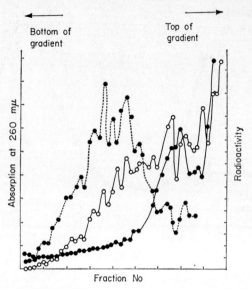

Fig. 3.14. The distribution of radioactivity among the different species of ribosomes after the incubation of the light microsome fraction from young rat liver with [14C]leucine. Optical density – ●–●–●, total radioactivity. ○–○–○–, specific radioactivity based on RNA ●...●...●. [From P. N. Campbell, G. Serck-Hanssen and E. Lowe, *Biochem. J.*, **97**, 422 (1965).]

may well be stabilized by membranes for the ratio of RNA to protein is not as great as with the free ribosomes but is considerably greater than with the bound ribosomes.

Noll and his colleagues in Pittsburgh were the first to detect the presence of polysomes in fractions of rat liver that had been carefully treated with deoxycholate. (These authors named the particles ergosomes but since ergosomes appear to have similar properties to polysomes extracted from reticulocytes it is less confusing to use the same name for all such particles.) If the sedimentation constant of the mixture of such particles is determined, most of the constituents are found to have a low one corresponding to the presence of monomers and dimers. Noll devised a method of concentrating the larger

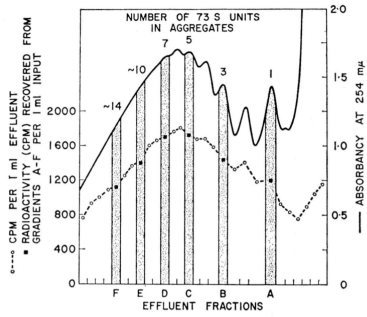

FIG. 3.15. Fractionation of polysomes according to aggregate size.
The dotted line shows the determination based on radioactivity de-
termination and the full line based on sedimentation properties.
(From T. Staehelin *et al.*, ref. 32.)

particles by centrifuging the deoxycholate-treated fraction through a
zone of high density sucrose (1·5–2·0 M). In this way Noll demonstrated, as seen in Fig. 3.15,[32] the presence of particles containing
1–14 ribosomes.

We see, therefore, that the RNP particle preparation previously
described and which Korner had shown to incorporate amino acids
into protein, consists mainly of monomeric units but also contains a
variety of polymers containing up to 14 ribosomes. The activity of
such an RNP particle fraction is even less susceptible to poly U[28]
than is the microsome fraction from which it was derived and is very
much less stimulated than the free ribosomes. This finding is con-

sistent with the idea that the RNP particle fraction consists mainly of degraded polysomes so that even the monomeric units consist of a ribosome linked to a small piece of m-RNA, what may be described as a monomeric polysome or monosome. From work on reticulocyte polysomes it is clear that deoxycholate itself does not break up polysomes. It seems more likely that in the course of the removal of the membrane a diesterase is activated and it is this that degrades the liver polysomes.

The concept of the RNP particle fraction containing degraded polysomes also explains another finding. Although such a fraction actively incorporates amino acids into protein, it is comparatively inactive for the synthesis of serum albumin compared with the whole microsome fraction.[33] As shown in Fig. 3.16 the only degraded polysomes that will be able to complete the synthesis of serum albumin will be those which contain pieces of m-RNA from the end of the polysome. The other degraded polysomes will incorporate amino acid into their peptide chains as the ribosomes move along the short pieces of m-RNA, but this will not be detected as albumin synthesis. This is a good example of how important it is in these isolated systems to study the synthesis of a specific protein rather than the mere incorporation of amino acids into uncharacterized protein.

So far as the role of the morphological constituents of the liver cell in protein synthesis is concerned the situation can be summarized in Fig. 3.17. The evidence is that ribosomes attached to the endoplasmic reticulum in the form of polysomes synthesize albumin and other proteins, which, if they are to be exported, are then transferred to the inside of the membrane. The free polysomes make protein, so far uncharacterized, while the free ribosomes, lacking

FIG. 3.16. Diagrammatic representation of serum albumin synthesis by a polysome. The diagram indicates that when the polysome is disrupted the maximum chain length that the resulting units can synthesize when incubated will depend on the position the unit occupied in the original polysome. Thus only units which contain a ribosome from position 20 can synthesize the entire polypeptide chain of serum albumin containing 574 amino acid residues.

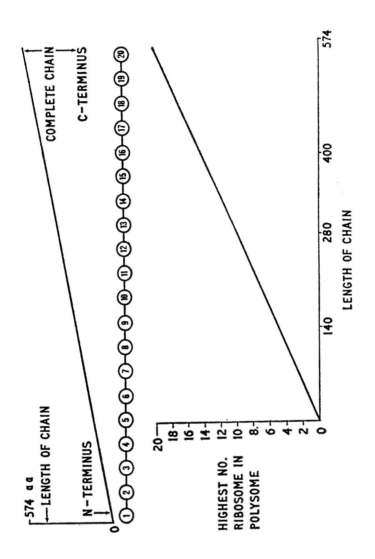

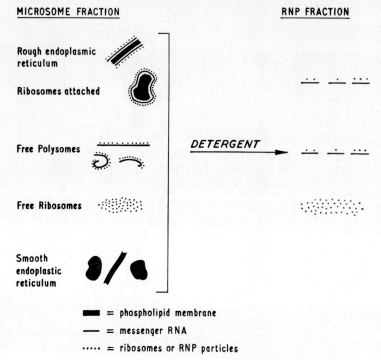

MICROSOME FRACTION　　　　　　　　　　　　**RNP FRACTION**

Rough endoplasmic reticulum

Ribosomes attached

Free Polysomes　　　　　　　　　　*DETERGENT* →

Free Ribosomes

Smooth endoplastic reticulum

■■■ = phospholipid membrane

—— = messenger RNA

····· = ribosomes or RNP particles

FIG. 3.17. Diagrammatic representation of the morphological components of the microsome fraction from rat liver and the action of a detergent such as deoxycholate on it.

messenger RNA, are inactive. The latter are probably the products of protein synthesis on the polysomes. The smooth membrane seems to play no part in protein synthesis but probably assists in exporting the protein synthesized by ribosomes of the rough surfaced membrane.

Special Features of Components from Tissues other than Liver in Protein Synthesis

One of the reasons for dealing at length with liver is that in many respects it is multifunctional and therefore representative of cells in general. There are, however, certain other tissues that have interesting features not found in liver.

Palade, Siekevitz *et al.* have examined closely the protein synthesizing activity of the exocrine cell of the pancreas of the guinea-pig. The pancreas is particularly interesting because it makes many well-characterized enzymes. As was explained in Chapter 1, these enzymes are often, as with chymotrypsin and trypsin, synthesized in an inactive form or zymogen. They are then exported from the cell as zymogen granules. In the case of ribonuclease, which is also made in the pancreas, no inactive form has so far been detected and this may be the reason why in general it is not possible to detect synthetic activity in subcellular particles from this tissue. The only exception is for some preparations from dog and ox which have been studied by Dickman.[34]

Figure 3.18 shows typical results from the work of Palade and Siekevitz for the incorporation of radioactive amino acid into the proteins of the different particles of guinea-pig pancreas. It will be seen that although the microsome fraction is active in this respect the mitochondrial and zymogen fractions are also very active. The reason is that both these fractions contain zymogen granules which are difficult to separate from mitochondria and the granules, of course, contain the newly synthesized protein. The rough endoplasmic reticulum is very prominent in this cell as can be seen from Plate I.3 and also in higher magnification in Plate III.7.

When the microsome fraction is examined the fragmented cysternae of the reticulum are seen to have broken up and formed vesicles as seen in Plate III.8. The vesicles in this fraction from pancreas are more susceptible to changes in osmotic condition than are those from liver. Whether they be blown up or deflated depends on the tonicity of the medium in which the fraction is suspended.

Caro and Palade[35] have made a detailed study of the formation of zymogen granules in the guinea-pig pancreas by a technique that combines ^{3}H-autoradiography and electron microscopy. They concluded that the zymogen granules are formed in the Golgi region by a progressive concentration of secretory products within large condensing vacuoles. The results are consistent with the transfer

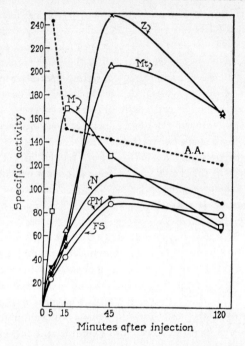

FIG. 3.18. Variation in time in the specific activities of proteins of guinea pig pancreas after injection of $[1-{}^{14}C]$ leucine. Z, zymogen fraction; Mt, mitochondrial fraction; N, nuclear fraction; M, microsomal fraction; PM, postmicrosomal fraction; FS, final supernatant fraction; A.A., amino acids in the acid extract of the final supernatant. [From P. Siekevitz and G. E. Palade, *J. biophys. biochem. Cytol.*, **4**, 557–66 (1958).]

of the zymogen from the rough endoplasmic reticulum to small smooth surfaced vesicles situated at the periphery of the Golgi complex and then to the centrally located condensing vacuoles. These findings filled in the missing details in the scheme drawn up by Siekevitz and Palade in their earlier work.[36] In this they showed that the last stage in the export of protein is for the zymogen granules to move away from the Golgi zone and accumulate progressively in the apical region of the cell. Here the granules wait to be released into the glandular lumina after the intake of food. Thus the membrane of a Golgi vacuole becomes the limiting membrane of a zymogen granule. During the discharge of the granule contents into the acinar lumen this membrane fuses and becomes continuous with the cell membrane. The above method of exporting protein is probably not confined to the pancreas.

So far we have been considering the synthesis of soluble proteins but many of the proteins synthesized by cells are large and fibrous and in many ways these must be more difficult for the cell to handle than the soluble ones. An example of such a large insoluble protein is collagen. This protein is characterized by its content of the unusual amino acid hydroxy-proline so that the presence of the amino acid identifies it. Collagen has recently been shown to be made on large polysomes.[37] Progress in this field has been slow, mainly because of the fibrous nature of the tissue that contains the cells that synthesize collagen, so that it has not been easy to break up the tissue and release the polysomes. This has now been successfully accomplished by disrupting the tissue in the presence of deoxycholate.[38]

The mammary gland is a particularly interesting site of protein synthesis because here the nature of the protein being made changes during the development of the gland. Thus during pregnancy the gland grows in size and the synthetic activity is confined to the growth of mammary tissue. At the onset of lactation the gland suddenly starts to make the proteins characteristic of milk. The latter are divided into casein and whey protein. The whey often contains one or more easily characterized proteins suitable for biosynthetic studies. Recently, the synthesis of α-lactalbumin, the main whey protein of the guinea-pig, has been studied.

Finally, one should perhaps indicate that there are many tissues from which it is very difficult to prepare a microsome fraction which has synthetic activity. Thus the kidney, for no known reason, fails to produce a microsome fraction with any activity at all. Similarly many tumours which are very active in protein synthesis *in vivo* yield subcellular fractions of low activity.

Properties of the Smooth Surfaced Reticulum

Although the microsome fraction is mainly noted for containing 40–50% of the RNA of the cell, in the case of liver it also contains about 50% of the phospholipid. For a similar fraction from the pancreas the concentration of lipid is only a mere eighth that of liver. This high concentration of phospholipid in the liver serves to remind us that the smooth surfaced reticulum plays a most important part in steroid and lipid metabolism and particularly in the export of these substances.

The smooth surfaced reticulum is the predominant form in the mature cells of the sebaceous glands which contain many secretory droplets.[39] In the interstitial cells of the opossum testis Lynn and Brown[40] have demonstrated that the enzymes involved in the production of testosterone from progesterone are present in the microsomes. That such enzymes are associated with the membrane component of the microsomes rather than the ribosomes is indicated by the fact that the enzymes were destroyed by lipases but were unaffected by ribonuclease.

Although all tissues so far studied are able to synthesize some cholesterol virtually all the plasma cholesterol is made in the liver and in this tissue 90% of the steroid is found in the microsomes.

PLATE III.7. High magnification of a small field in the basal region of a pancreatic exocrine cell of the rat. The field is occupied by numerous profiles of the endoplasmic reticulum, most of which are of elongated form and appear disposed in parallel rows. The membrane of the endoplasmic reticulum separates two distinct phases in the cytoplasm: one is represented by the light, homogeneous material enclosed in the cavities of the system; the other by the surrounding cytoplasmic matrix. Numerous small, dense particles, ~ 150 Å in diameter, appear attached to the outer surface of the membrane limiting the cavities of the endoplasmic reticulum. In addition to these attached particles, particles of comparable size and density occur apparently freely scattered in the cytoplasmic matrix. Magnification × 70,000. *m*, part of a mitochondrion; *rs*, endoplasmic reticulum, membrane of the reticulum sectioned normally (*n*), (*o*) when cut obliquely, (*f*) small windows in the walls of the cisternae; *c*, cavity of the *rs*, *mx* surrounding cytoplasmic matrix; *ap*, attached ribosomes; and *fp*, free particles. (From G. E. Palade, ref. 21.)

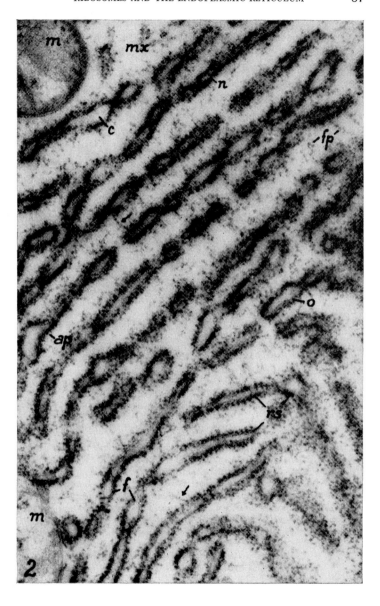

The cholesterol is present in the membranes as a phospholipid complex which may be important in the physico-chemical problems involved in its synthesis. Thus cholesterol, which is lipid but not water soluble, is formed from acetate which is water soluble, the reaction being catalysed by enzymes present probably in the protein moiety of the membrane—which is itself rich in phospholipid. The phospholipid, which is both water and lipid soluble, therefore, fulfils an important role in bringing the water soluble substrate and enzyme into close juxtaposition to the lipid soluble product.

There is a tendency for the smooth endoplasmic reticulum to be present in the peripheral area of the liver cell and it is here too that the glycogen accumulates. When an animal is fasted overnight the amount of glycogen in the liver rapidly diminishes and the fact that under such conditions the amount of smooth reticulum was also reduced has in the past been considered as evidence that glycogen synthesis took place in the smooth reticulum. However, if the smooth reticulum is isolated, it is found that it does not contain the enzymes involved in glycogen synthesis and so it is no longer believed to be concerned in this process.[41]

Remmer and Merker[42] from Berlin showed that if one feeds fat soluble drugs such as phenobarbitone to an animal there is a marked increase in the amount of the enzymes that destroy the drugs. The drugs also cause an increase in the amount of smooth reticulum compared with rough reticulum. Orrenius and his colleagues in Stockholm find that feeding barbitone first induces the synthesis of

---

PLATE III.8. Section through a microsome pellet isolated by centrifugation from a guinea-pig pancreas disrupted in 0·88 M sucrose. The microsomes are small, closed vesicles limited by a thin membrane which bears ribosomes on the outside. The apparent heterogeneity of the fraction is due primarily to sectioning. Those in median section are marked mv_1, others are cut medially mv_2, others are cut laterally mv_3. The microsomal content varies widely in density from light mv_1 to medium mv_4 and high mv_5. A ruptured microsomal vesicle mv_6 contains an intracisternal granule. Magnification × 72,000. [From G. E. Palade, in *Microsomal Particles and Protein Synthesis* (Ed. by R. B. Roberts), Pergamon Press, Oxford, 1958.]

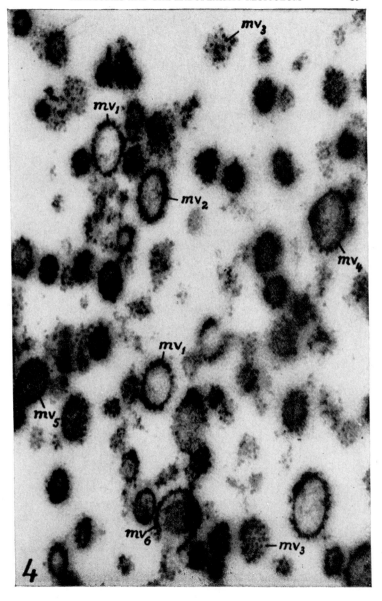

enzymes in the rough reticulum and that the two types of reticulum are interconvertible.[43] Both the increase in enzymes and in the amount of reticulum is inhibited by administration of either actinomycin D or puromycin suggesting that new protein synthesis is induced by the drug. Since the drug is lipid soluble the synthesis of new membranes represents an adaptive change which effectively brings together the drug and the enzymes responsible for its detoxication. This finding, therefore, emphasizes again the close connection between lipid metabolism and the smooth reticulum.

Enzymes and the Endoplasmic Reticulum

The first person to study the presence of enzymes in the liver microsomes was Hogeboom in 1949.[44] He found that they contained NADH and a NADPH cytochrome c reductase but did not contain succinic dehydrogenase.

In 1950 Hers and de Duve[45] in Belgium showed that glucose 6-phosphatase, an important enzyme in the degradation of glycogen to glucose, was confined to the microsome fraction of the liver. Since then there have been many attempts to render this enzyme soluble, but so far without any convincing success, so that it must be concluded that the enzyme is firmly bound to the membranes. This is a very useful finding in that the presence of glucose 6-phosphatase serves as a convenient marker for endoplasmic reticulum.

Mueller and Miller[46] in 1949, showed that the liver microsomes catalyse the demethylation of dimethylaminoazobenzene. The microsomes have since been found to perform a number of detoxication reactions all involving the NADPH oxidase system. Hochstein and Ernster[47] in Stockholm find that liver microsomes catalyse a rapid peroxidation of their endogenous lipids.

Treatment of the microsome fraction with differing concentrations of deoxycholate leads to a variation in the proportion of enzyme activity that is released into the soluble fraction so that some enzymes seem to be released more readily than others. At the one extreme we have seen that glucose 6-phosphatase is tightly bound to the membranes, whereas at the other extreme an enzyme like nucleoside diphosphatase is very easily released and is assumed to be retained within the vesicles in a soluble form. The exact distribution of the various enzymes between the two extremes is the subject of further study.[48]

Dallner[29] has made good use of caesium and magnesium salts to assist in the subfractionation of the smooth and rough fractions. These salts are bound to the ribosomes on the rough endoplasmic reticulum which renders it denser than the smooth reticulum and so enables the two components to be separated by density gradient centrifugation. By this means Dallner has succeeded in separating the microsomes into one rough fraction and two smooth. He finds that one of the smooth fractions contains glucose 6-phosphatase while the other does not. This finding certainly suggests that there may well be two clear cut fractions of smooth reticulum. So far there have been no suggestions as to the role of the cytochrome b_5 in the microsome fraction.

References

1. M. B. HOAGLAND, E. B. KELLER and P. C. ZAMECNIK, Enzymatic carboxyl activation of amino acids, *J. biol. Chem.*, **218**, 345–58 (1956).
2. M. B. HOAGLAND, M. L. STEPHENSON, J. F. SCOTT, L. I. HECHT and P. C. ZAMECNIK, A soluble ribonucleic acid intermediate in protein synthesis, *J. biol. Chem.*, **231**, 241–57 (1958).
3. R. W. HOLLEY, J. APGAR, G. A. EVERETT, J. T. MADISON, M. MARQUISSEE, S. H. MERRITT, J. R. PENSWICK and A. ZAMU, Structure of an RNA, *Science*, **147**, 1462–5 (1965).
4. P. LEDER and M. NIRENBERG, RNA code-words and protein synthesis II, *Proc. nat. Acad. Sci. Wash.*, **52**, 420–7 (1964).
5. S. SLAPIKOFF, J. M. FESSENDEN and K. MOLDAVE, Enzymatic incorporation of amino acid from aminoacyl soluble ribonucleic acid into ribosomal ribonucleic acid and ribosomal protein, *J. biol. Chem.*, **238**, 1479–84 (1963).
6. S. BRENNER, F. JACOB and M. MESELSON, An unstable intermediate carrying information from genes to ribosomes for protein synthesis *Nature, Lond.*, 1961, **190**, 576–85 (1961).
7. M. W. NIRENBERG and J. H. MATTHAEI, The dependence of cell-free protein synthesis in *E. Coli* upon naturally occurring or synthetic polynucleotides, *Proc. nat. Acad. Sci. Wash.*, **47**, 1588–602 (1961).

8. M. NIRENBERG, P. LEDER, M. BERNFELD, R. BRIMACOMBE, J. TRUPIN, F. ROTTMAN and C. O'NEAL, RNA code-words and protein synthesis VII. On the general nature of the RNA code, *Proc. nat. Acad. Sci. Wash.*, **53**, 1161–8 (1965).

9. H. E. HUXLEY and G. ZUBAY, Electron microscope observations on the structure of microsomal particles from *Escherichia coli*, *J. molec. Biol.*, **2**, 10–18 (1960).

10. M. TAL and D. ELSON, The location of ribonuclease in *Escherichia coli*, *Biochim. biophys. Acta*, **76**, 40–7 (1963).

11. A. S. SPIRIN, N. A. KISELEV, R. S. SHAKULOV and A. A. BOGDANOV, Study of the structure of the ribosomes, reversible unfolding of the ribosome particles in ribonucleoprotein strands, and a model of the packing, *Biokhimiya*, **28**, 920–30 (1963).

12. W. GILBERT, Polypeptide synthesis in *E. Coli* I, *J. molec. Biol.*, **6**, 374–88 (1963); M. CANNON, R. KRUG and W. GILBERT, The binding of S–RNA by *Escherichia coli* ribosomes, *J. molec. Biol.*, **7**, 360–78 (1963).

13. J. R. WARNER and A. RICH, The number or soluble RNA molecules on a reticulocyte polyribosome, *Proc. nat. Acad. Sci. Wash.*, **51**, 1134–41 (1964).

14. J. R. WARNER, P. M. KNOPF and A. RICH, A multiple ribosomal structure in protein synthesis, *Proc. nat. Acad. Sci. Wash.*, **49**, 122–9 (1963); J. R. WARNER, A. RICH and C. E. HALL, Electron microscope studies of ribosomal clusters synthesizing hemoglobin, *Science*, **138**, 1399–403 (1962).

15. A. R. WILLIAMSON and R. SCHWEET, Role of the genetic message in polyribosome function, *J. molec. Biol.* **11**, 358–72 (1965).

16. M. D. SCHARFF, A. J. SHATKIN and L. LEVINTOU, Association of newly formed viral protein with specific polyribosomes, *Proc. nat. Acad. Sci. Wash.*, **50**, 686–93 (1963).

17. T. O. CASPERSSON, *Cell Growth and Cell Function*, Norton, New York, 1950.

18. J. BRACHET in *The Nucleic Acids*, Vol. II (Ed. E. CHARGAFF and J. N. DAVIDSON), p. 475. Academic Press, New York, 1955.

19. A. CLAUDE, The constitution of protoplasm, *Science*, **97**, 451–6 (1943).

20. G. E. PALADE and P. SIEKEVITZ, Liver microsomes. An integrated morphological and biochemical study, *J. biophys. biochem. Cytol.*, **2**, 171–98 (1956).

21. R. B. ROBERTS in *Microsomal Particles and Protein Synthesis* (Ed. R. B. ROBERTS), p. 8, Pergamon Press, Oxford, 1958.

22. H. BORSOOK, C. L. DEASY, A. J. HAAGEN–SMIT, G. KEIGHLEY and P. H. LOWRY, Metabolism of C^{14}-labelled glycine, L-histidine, L-leucine and L-lysine, *J. biol. Chem.*, **187**, 839–48 (1950).

23. T. HULTIN, Incorporation *in vivo* of ^{15}N-labeled glycine into liver fractions of newly hatched chicks, *Exp. Cell Res.*, **1**, 376–81 (1950).

24. P. C. ZAMECNIK and E. B. KELLER, Relation between phosphate energy donors and incorporation of labelled amino acids into proteins, *J. biol. Chem.*, **209**, 337–54 (1954).

25. A. KORNER, Incorporation *in vitro* of [^{14}C]amino acids into proteins of rat-liver microsomal particles, *Biochim. biophys. Acta*, **35**, 554–5 (1959).

26. R. SCHWEET, H. LAMFROM and E. ALLEN, The synthesis of hemoglobin in a cell-free system, *Proc. nat. Acad. Sci. Wash.*, **44**, 1029–35 (1958); J. BISHOP, J. LEAHY and R. SCHWEET, Formation of the peptide chain of hemoglobin, *Proc. nat. Acad. Sci. Wash.*, **46**, 1030–8 (1960).

27. T. PETERS, jun., The biosynthesis of rat serum albumin II, *J. biol. Chem.*, **237**, 1186–9 (1962).

28. J. R. SARGENT and P. N. CAMPBELL, The sequential synthesis of the polypeptide chain of serum albumin by the microsome fraction of rat liver, *Biochem. J.*, **96**, 134–46 (1965).

29. G. DALLNER, Studies on the structural and enzymic organisation of the membranous elements of liver microsomes, *Acta path. microbiol. scand.*, suppl. 166, 1–94 (1963).

30. E. C. HENSHAW, T. B. BOJARSKI, and H. H. HIATT, Protein synthesis by free and bound rat liver ribosomes *in vivo* and *in vitro*, *J. molec. Biol.*, **7**, 122–9 (1963).

31. I. T. OLIVER, W. F. C. BLUMER and I. J. WITHAM, Free ribosomes during maturation of rat liver, *Comp. Biochem. Physiol.*, **10**, 33–8 (1963).

32. T. STAEHELIN, F. O. WETTSTEIN, H. OURA and H. NOLL, Determination of the coding ratio based on molecular weight of messenger ribonucleic acid associated with ergosomes of different aggregate size, *Nature, Lond.*, **201**, 264–70 (1964).

33. A. VON DER DECKEN and P. N. CAMPBELL, Studies on the synthesis of serum albumin by ribonucleoprotein particles isolated from rat liver, *Biochem. J.*, **84**, 449–55 (1962).

34. S. R. DICKMAN and E. BRUENGER, Incorporation of amino acids into protein by intra-cellular particles from dog pancreas, *Biochim. biophys. Acta.*, **63**, 522–4 (1962); G. GAZZINELLI and S. R. DICKMAN, Incorporation of amino acids into protein by beef-pancreas ribosomes, *Biochim. biophys. Acta.*, **61**, 980–1 (1962).

35. L. G. CARO and G. E. PALADE, Protein synthesis, storage and discharge in the pancreatic exocrine cell, *J. Cell Biol.*, **20**, 473–95 (1964).

36. P. SIEKEVITZ and G. E. PALADE, A cytochemical study on the pancreas of the guinea-pig V, *J. biophys. biochem. Cytol.*, **7**, 619–30 (1960).

37. R. H. KRETSINGER, G. MANNER, B. S. GOULD and A. RICH, Synthesis of collagen on polyribosomes, *Nature, Lond.*, **202**, 438–41 (1964).

38. J. R. FLORINI and C. B. BREUER, Amino acid incorporation into protein by cell-free preparations from rat skeletal muscle III, *Biochemistry*, **4**, 253–7 (1965).

39. S. L. PALAY in *Frontiers in Cytology* (Ed. S. L. PALAY), p. 350, Yale Univ. Press, 1958.

40. W. S. LYNN, jun. and R. H. BROWN, The conversion of progesterone to androgens by testes, *J. biol. Chem.*, **232**, 1015–30 (1958).

41 J. P. REVEL, L. NAPOLITANO and D. W. FAWCETT, Identification of glycogen in electron micrographs of thin tissue sections, *J. biophys. biochem. Cytol.*, **8**, 575–89 (1960).

E

42. H. REMMER and H. J. MERKER, Drug induced changes in the liver endoplasmic reticulum associated with drug-metabolizing enzymes, *Science*, **142**, 1657 (1963).

43. S. ORRENIUS, J. I. E. ERICSSON and L. ERNSTER, Phonobarbital induced synthesis of the microsomal drug metabolizing enzyme system and its relationship to the proliferation of endoplasmic membranes. A morphological and biochemical study, *J. Cell Biol.*, **25**, 627–39 (1965); S. ORRENIUS, Further studies on the induction of the drug-hydroxylating enzyme system of liver microsomes, *J. Cell Biol.*, **26**, 725–33 (1965).

44. G. H. HOGEBOOM, Cytochemical studies of mammalian tissues II. The distribution of diphosphopyridine nucleotide cytochrome *c* reductase in rat liver fractions, *J. biol. Chem.*, **177**, 847–58 (1949).

45. H. G. HERS and C. DE DUVE, Le systéme hexose phosphatasique II, *Bull. Soc. chim. Biol.*, **32**, 20–29 (1950).

46. G. C. MUELLER and J. A. MILLER, The reductive cleavage of 4-dimethylaminoazobenzene by rat liver; the intracellular distribution of the enzyme system and its requirement for triphosphopyridine nucleotide, *J. biol. Chem.*, **180**, 1125–36 (1949).

47. P. HOCHSTEIN and L. ERNSTER, Microsomal peroxidation of lipides and its possible role in cell injury, *CIBA Foundation Symp. on Cellular Injury*, 123–34 (1964).

48. L. ERNSTER, P. SIEKEVITZ and G. E. PALADE, Enzyme-structure relationships in the endoplasmic reticulum of rat liver, *J. Cell Biol.*, **15**, 541–62 (1962).

Further Reading

P. N. CAMPBELL, The synthesis of proteins by the cytoplasmic components of animal cells, *Biol. Rev.*, **35**, 413–58 (1960).

P. N. CAMPBELL, The biosynthesis of proteins, *Progress in Biophys. and Molec. Biology*, **15**, 3–38 (1965).

A. RICH, Polyribosomes, *Scientific American*, December 1963.

M. W. NIRENBERG, The Genetic Code II, *Scientific American*, March 1963.

F. H. C. CRICK, The Genetic Code, *Scientific American*, October 1962.

J. HURWITZ and J. J. FURTH, Messenger RNA, *Scientific American*, February 1962.

M. L. PETERMANN, *The Physical and Chemical Properties of Ribosomes*, Elsevier, Amsterdam, 1964.

K. MCQUILLEN, Ribosomes and the synthesis of proteins, *Progress Biophys. Biophysical Chem.*, **12**, 67–106 (1961).

P. C. ZAMECNIK, Unsolved problems in the biosynthesis of proteins, *Biochem. J.*, **85**, 257–64 (1962).

M. A. EPSTEIN, The fine structure of animal cells; a brief introductory survey, *J. Linnean Soc.*, **44**, 153–63 (1959).

Microsomal Particles and Protein Synthesis (Ed. by R. B. ROBERTS), 1st Symp. Biophysical Society, Pergamon Press, London, 1958. This contains a chapter by G. E. Palade on "Microsomes and ribonucleoprotein particles".

H. R. V. ARNSTEIN, The structure and function of ribosomes in protein biosynthesis, *Ann. Rep. Chem. Soc.*, 512–28 (1964).

P. N. CAMPBELL, Protein synthesis with special reference to growth processes both normal and abnormal, *Adv. in Cancer Res.*, **5**, 97–155 (1958).

P. N. CAMPBELL, The synthesis of serum albumin by the microsome fraction of the liver, *Protein Biosynthesis* (Ed. by R. J. C. HARRIS), pp. 19–34, Academic Press, London, 1961.

H. CHANTRENNE. *The Biosynthesis of Proteins*, Pergamon Press, Oxford, 1961.

R. SCHWEET, J. BISHOP and A. MORRIS, Protein synthesis with particular reference to hemoglobin synthesis—A review, *Lab. Investigation*, **10**, 992–1011 (1961).

Y. MOULÉ, Endoplasmic reticulum and microsomes of rat liver, *Cellular Membranes in Development*, Academic Press, New York, 1964.

Biological Structure and Function (Ed. by T. W. GOODWIN and O. LINDBERG), Vol. I and Vol. II, Academic Press, London 1961.

CHAPTER 4

The Nucleus

ALL animal and plant cells contain at least one nucleus which is clearly surrounded by an envelope. Although bacteria contain a nuclear region, this has no circumscribing membrane. The only obvious exception to these statements is the red blood cell in mammals either in the form of the mature cell, the erythrocyte, or less mature cell, the reticulocyte. These forms contain no nucleus but the erythroblast of the bone marrow from which they both derive is nucleated.

Although the nucleus was the first cell component to be isolated, by Miescher in 1871, its morphological analysis is much less advanced than that of the cytoplasm. It is for this reason that it has seemed best in this book to consider the structure and function of the nucleus after that of the endoplasmic reticulum and not before.

Morphological Components

In considering the structure of the nucleus it is necessary to differentiate between the various phases of activity of the cell. This is because when the cell is undergoing division, the nuclear contents are dispersed and the appearance of the nucleus differs markedly from that when the cell is said to be resting. Mirsky and Osawa[1] have preferred the term "interphase nucleus" since this is purely descriptive and does not involve any consideration of metabolic activity. Since virtually nothing is known about biochemical events leading to the initiation of cell division, it is proposed to confine our attention to the interphase nucleus, except when considering the synthesis of DNA.

The size and shape of nuclei differ markedly among cell types. The nuclei of many cells, including those of the liver, are round, whereas those of muscle fibres are elongated and those of polymorpholeucocytes irregular. In the silk spinning cells of insect larvae the nuclei are branched.

The nucleus is the depository of the genes or Mendelian factors, of which the primary chemical substance is DNA. DNA can be detected microscopically by the application of the Feulgen stain. This consists of treating the cell with warm dilute HCl, transferring to a solution containing decolorized magenta and then washing with dilute H_2SO_4. The DNA stains red–violet due to the presence of deoxyribose which restores the colour of the magenta. There are great differences between the DNA content of the nuclei of different cells as revealed by Feulgen staining. Thus sperm nuclei may have as much as 60% DNA whereas somatic cells have much less; in the case of calf liver only 16%. Egg nuclei have the lowest amount and in the egg of the sea urchin the presence of DNA is barely detectable.

DNA has for long been claimed to be entirely confined to the nucleus. While this is still virtually true, it is now clear that some is present in the mitochondria as already mentioned in Chapter 2. The DNA in the nucleus is complexed with a basic protein called a histone to form a nucleohistone. The nature and function of the histones will be considered later. The interesting thing about the content of DNA in a cell is that it is constant. Thus the amount of DNA in all the somatic cells of one particular species of animal is the same and this amount is twice that found in the germ cells of the particular species. The amount of DNA per particular chromosome is fixed and is characteristic of that species. One can change the nutritional or metabolic state of the animal but the amount of DNA per cell is unaffected. As might be expected from this observation, the DNA of a cell in interphase is inert metabolically to the extent that it is not itself being built up or broken down. However, as we see later it is serving a very active catalytic role.

Plate IV.1 shows an electron micrograph of a nucleus isolated from a parenchymal liver cell of the guinea-pig. Three nucleoli

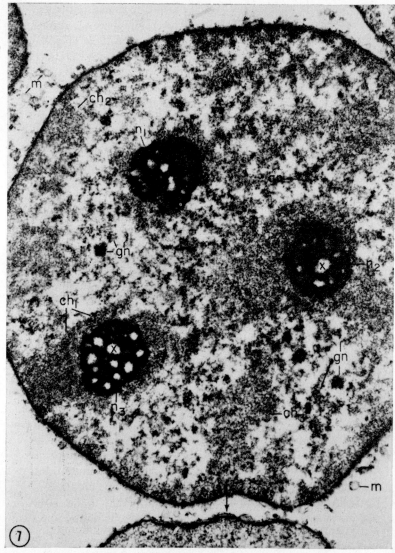

PLATE IV.1. Parts of four profiles of guinea-pig liver cell nuclei in a nuclear fraction isolated by the procedure of Maggio *et al.* (ref.

may be seen in this particular nucleus but similar nuclei may contain only one or two. The nucleoli are characterized by their dense granular texture and also contain lacunae. Other parts of the nuclei are characterized by the presence of regions of fine textured chromatin and in Plate IV.1 these are seen around the nucleoli, at the periphery immediately under the nuclear evelope, and also scattered throughout the nucleus. The remaining coarse granular material is not identified. As will be discussed later, there is ample evidence that in the intact cell the membranes of the envelope are continuous with the endoplasmic reticulum. It is not surprising, therefore, that in this and subsequent plates the presence of some of this material is seen in spite of the fact that these nuclei have been isolated from a cell suspension. The nature of the nuclear envelope is seen in Plate IV.2. It consists of two membranes with pores; ribosomes often being attached to the cytoplasmic surface of the outer membrane.

The nucleolus, which is not surrounded by a membrane, is apparent during interphase, disappears in the course of prophase and reappears at telophase. This cycle raises questions concerning the continuity of the nucleolus during mitosis. It seems probable that this component is formed by the organization of materials that are widely dispersed and closely associated with the chromosomes. Finer details of the internal structure of the nucleus are shown in Plate IV.3.

Chemical Composition

The content of DNA has already been described. When other

4). In the central profile, three nucleoli (n_1, n_2, n_3) show the dense granular texture that characterizes these bodies *in situ*. Some of their lacunae are, however, larger and of lighter content (x) than in intact cells. Fine textured chromatic regions appear (1) around the nucleoli (ch_1) (nucleolus-associated chromatin), (2) at the periphery of the nucleus, immediately below the nuclear envelope (ch_2), and (3) scattered throughout the rest of the profile (ch_3). The rest of the nucleus is occupied by a heterogeneous, coarsely granular material (gn). Nuclear envelopes can be seen at arrows. Contaminating microsomes are marked m. Magnification $\times$ 20,000. [From R. Maggio *et al.*, *J. Cell Biol.*, **18**, 267 (1963).]

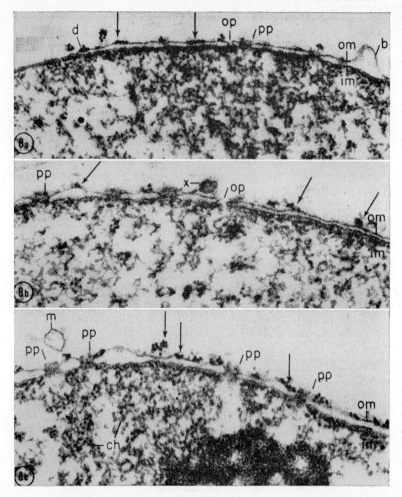

PLATE IV.2. Normal sections through nuclear envelopes in nuclear fractions from guinea-pig liver, isolated by procedure of Maggio *et al.* (ref. 4). The outer and inner membrane are marked *om* and *im* respectively. Ribosomes attached to the outer membrane are indicated by arrows. (a) The outer membrane shows a blob at *b* and is missing to the left of *d*. A number of nuclear pores are visible at *pp* and *op*, some of them appear "plugged" (*pp*), one is open (*op*).

substances are considered it is important to know the method whereby the nuclei were isolated from the cell and the morphology of the isolated preparation. In the last section it was seen that, for example, ribosomes either as such or as pieces of the rough endoplasmic reticulum are associated with the nuclear envelope, so that one must be clear as to the definition of a nucleus. It is necessary first, therefore, to mention the methods used for the isolation of nuclei.

Following the work of Stoneburg[2] it was usual to employ solutions containing citric acid which, although they facilitate the separation of nuclei from the cytoplasm, cause the precipitation of the nucleoplasm. In sucrose solution there is a tendency for the DNA to leak out which causes clumping since it is very viscous. Clumping must be avoided if only to prevent cytoplasmic contamination and can be prevented by adding Ca^{2+} ions or Mg^{2+} ions, to the sucrose solution. Chauveau,[3] the Franch cytologist, introduced a simple method that involves the use of very high concentrations (2·2 M) of sucrose. Maggio, Siekevitz and Palade[4] have modified this method using both 2·2 M sucrose and $CaCl_2$ and this leads to a homogeneous fraction of well preserved nuclei from liver; the only defect being that the yield is only 25%. This could mean that the sample was not representative of the total nuclear population. Rather similar methods giving a better yield of nuclei based on DNA have been described by Widnell and Tata,[5] and also by Sporn.[6]

The gross composition of liver nuclei isolated by the Maggio method was RNA 4·7%, DNA 22·3% and protein 73%, when the sum of these components was taken as 100%. Lipid and carbohydrate were not determined. The ratio of DNA to RNA varied

---

Magnification × 52,000. (b) Plugged (*pp*) and unplugged (*op*) pores are shown at a higher magnification than in (a). The body marked *x* might be a displaced plug (annulus). Magnification × 65,000. (c). The micrograph shows clearly the nuclear envelope, with a series of plugged pores (*pp*) and a tenuously attached microsomal vesicle (*m*). Part of the nucleolus is visible in the lower quarter. Chromation masses are marked *ch*. Magnification × 75,000. [From R. Maggio *et al.*, *J. Cell Biol.*, **18**, 267 (1963).]

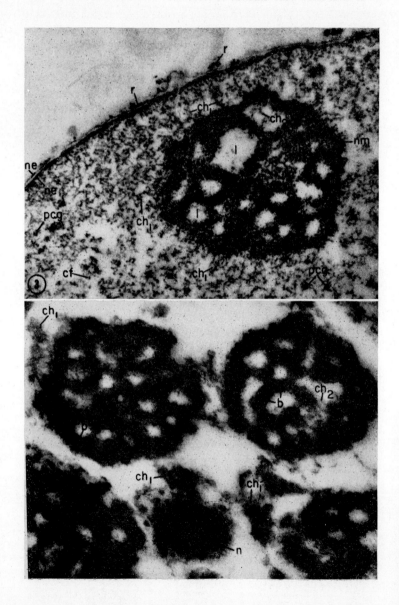

from 3·8 to 5·6. It can be calculated that the nuclei contain 8–10% of the RNA in the cell. The RNA of the cytoplasmic fraction is easily extracted with phosphate buffer so that it is of interest that only 3% of the RNA in nuclei could be extracted in this way. It is not surprising that the results obtained on the chemical composition of nuclei by different workers using various methods of isolation show a good deal of variation (see review by Roodyn).

The successful isolation of nucleoli depends on a method which will rupture the nuclear envelope while preserving the organelle. It is also necessary to prevent gel formation by DNA since this would render differential centrifugation difficult. Disruption has been performed either by using osmotic effects, e.g. homogenization in a high density medium, by ultrasonic vibration, by forcing the material through a small aperture or by chelating all the Ca^{2+} ions in the nuclei.

Maggio[7] has used ultrasonic vibrations to break up the nuclei from guinea-pig liver and then separated the nucleoli from the nucleoplasm by sucrose density gradient centrifugation. In the electron microscope the nucleoplasm consisted of fragments of

PLATE IV.3. *Top:* Part of an isolated nucleus in a nuclear fraction prepared from guinea-pig liver. The nucleus shows a large nucleolus surrounded and penetrated by chromatin threads (ch_1 and ch_2 respectively). The nucleolar mass (nm) has a distinct fine granular texture. The nucleolar lacunae (l) appear distended and "empty". The nuclear envelope marked nc bears attached ribosomes (r) on its outer surface. The nucleoplasm contains in addition to chromatin threads, some large, dense granules (pcg) and clusters of fibrillar and/or granular material of finer texture (cf). Magnification $\times$ 47,000. *Bottom:* Nucleolar subfraction. A comparison with *top* shows that isolated nucleoli retain the size and general morphology they have in intact nuclei, the nucleolar mass appears, however, more compact and as a result its granular texture is less clearly visible. Most lacunae are "empty" and seem to be limited by a relatively sharp boundary (b). The chromatin threads have aggregated into coarser strands ch_1, ch_2 than in intact nuclei and appear as pale, relatively homogeneous masses either in the lacunae (ch_2) or at the periphery of the nucleoli (ch_1). The nucleolus marked n, just grazed by the section, shows no cut open lacuna. Magnification $\times$ 47,000. [From R. Maggio *et al.*, *J. Cell Biol.*, **18**, 293 (1963).]

chromatin threads of various sizes but the fate of the nuclear membrane was unknown.

The nucleoli isolated by the above method contained 6–11% of the original nuclear mass and consisted of about 4% RNA, 9–10% DNA and 86–87% protein. The corresponding figures for the nucleoplasmic fractions were 2%, 10–14% and 84–88% (RNA + DNA + protein = 100%). In terms of DNA and protein, RNA was 2 times more concentrated in the nucleolar than in the nucleoplasmic fractions. It seems possible to conclude that this RNA is chromatin or chromosome-associated RNA. If all the nucleolar DNA is considered to be due to chromatin contamination then about 40% of the nucleolar RNA must also be of chromatin origin. Extraction of the RNA of the nucleoli and nucleoplasm with 1 M NaCl showed that the types of RNA differed and this was confirmed by the base ratio determinations. They also concluded that the nucleoplasm possessed at least two DNA species but we shall return to the function of the nucleoli later.

Metabolism of Nucleic Acids—Biochemical Aspects

This is such a large subject that it is intended only to consider a few points that are of particular interest in linking morphology and function. The general outline of protein and nucleic acid synthesis was summarized in Chapter 3. The biochemical functions of the nucleus are two. Firstly, it acts as a storehouse in the cell of the genetic information which upon cell division is duplicated exactly for the daughter cells. Secondly, it acts as a storehouse for the information that determines the nature and amount of protein which is synthesized in the cytoplasm. As has already been indicated in Chapter 3, the genetic material is DNA so that it is necessary now to consider briefly its structure.

DNA structure

The chemical structure of a tetranucleotide portion of DNA is shown in Fig. 4.1. The entire molecule has, of course, a molecular weight of many millions containing millions of such nucleotides.

Each nucleotide differs only from its neighbour in the nature of the base it contains which can be one of four, two purines (adenine and guanine) and two pyrimidines (cytosine and thymine); genetic information is based on the sequence in which the bases occur in the polynucleotide. The great discovery of Watson and Crick[8] was that DNA is double-stranded and that the two chains run in opposite directions and are curled around each other to form a double helix (see Fig. 3.3). The chains are held together by the hydrogen bonding that takes place between pairs of bases, one member of each pair being a purine and one a pyrimidine. Thus adenine shares hydrogen atoms with thymine, and guanine shares them with cytosine as shown in Fig. 4.2. The general layout of the two chains is shown in Fig. 4.3. Since the original discovery there has been ample confirmation of this structure.

So far only one sample of DNA has been found which is single stranded and this is from a bacterial virus.[9] The chromosome of a coli bacterium contains 10^7 nucleotide pairs. The number of pairs in a single human sperm cell is of the order of 10^9 which corresponds to an actual length of DNA of 1 m.

DNA synthesis

The way in which DNA replicates has, in the main, been worked out by Kornberg[10] and his colleagues, now in California. He showed that it was the deoxymononucleoside triphosphates that served as the substrates for the enzyme which in the presence of a small amount of DNA led to the formation of phosphodiester bonds between adjacent nucleotides with the elimination of pyrophosphate. The reaction may be summarized as follows:

$$n \, d \, TPPP$$
$$n \, d \, GPPP$$
$$n \, d \, APPP + DNA \xrightarrow[\text{polymerase}]{\text{DNA}} [-dTP -dGP - dAP$$
$$n \, d \, CPPP \qquad\qquad - dCP]n + 4 \, (n) \, PP$$

The DNA primer specifies the order of bases in the newly synthesized DNA so that the ratio of the various nucleotides in the synthesized DNA are the same as those in the primer.[11] In this reaction we are thinking of the primer DNA as consisting of one strand of polynucleotide whereas, as already explained, DNA is really composed of two strands. In terms of the analogy of a photographic process, each strand bears a relation to the other of a positive and negative. Thus during duplication the positive primer leads to the synthesis of a negative and the negative primer to a positive. The two copies formed would together be identical to the original DNA duplex. The DNA polymerase does in fact copy both strands but in order to do so they must first separate. It is possible to heat DNA under conditions whereby the two strands come apart,

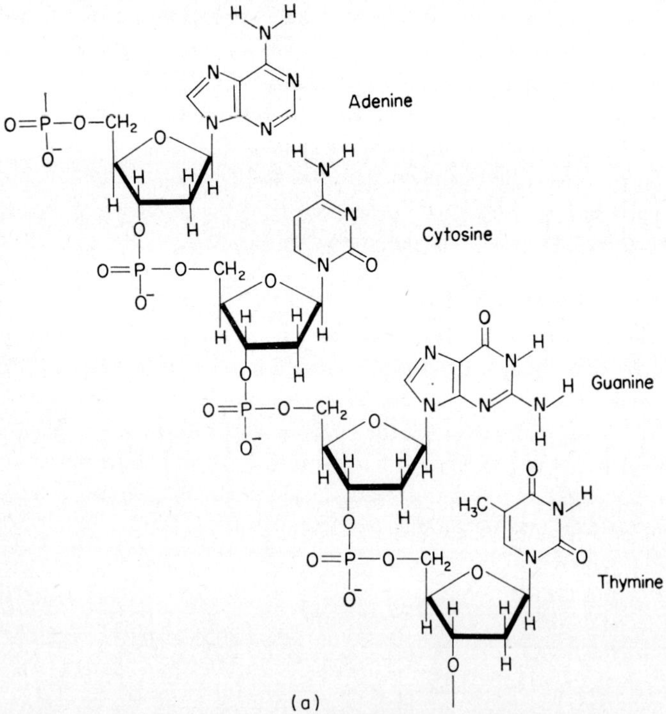

(a)

Fig. 4.1. A tetranucleotide sequence from (a) DNA and (b) RNA. (From M. F. Perutz, *Proteins and Nucleic Acids*, Elsevier, Amsterdam, 1962.)

(b)

a process known as "denaturation". This enzyme is primed much more effectively when such a denatured preparation of DNA is used rather than the "native" duplex DNA.

In the method of duplication described above only one strand of the primer DNA is passed on to the product. That DNA is in fact replicated in this way in the cell was first shown by Meselson and Stahl[12] in bacteria and later by Chun and Littlefield[13] using mammalian epithelial cells. Since in this process each daughter cell only receives one strand of the original DNA, it is described as "semi-conservative" (see Fig. 4.4).

The chromosome which can be seen in the cell by the light microscope at the prophase stage consists of at least two equivalent strands called chromatids. It is these chromatids that will eventually be separated from each other. It has been demonstrated by Taylor[14] that the chromosomes of the plant *Vicia* replicate in exactly the same way as we have described for DNA. However, we have as yet

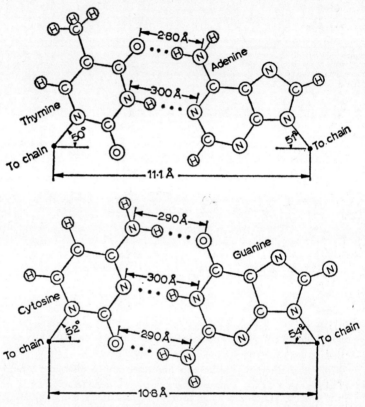

FIG. 4.2. Hydrogen bonding between the paired bases in DNA.
(From M. F. Perutz.)

no idea of the molecular organization of the chromatid. It appears that somehow the double-helix configuration of individual DNA molecules is reflected in the coiling of thousands of times larger chromosomes. At the morphological level the duplicating structure might be a whole chromosome, a chromatid or an even smaller unit.

Recently, Cairns[15] in Australia has shown that *E. coli* contains a DNA which is circular, having no free ends, and he has shown by radioautography how this replicates. In animal cells no natural

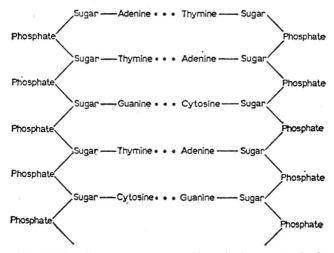

FIG. 4.3. Complementary sequences of bases in the two strands of the double helix [From M. F. Perutz.)

DNA has been shown to be circular but that of the polyoma virus which transmits certain types of tumours in animals is also circular.[16] As Crick[17] pointed out "it is remarkable that not only can a circle of DNA of 1 mm length be replicated but that the two daughter molecules can separate into separate regions without getting hopelessly tangled together".

The experiments on which most of the above conclusions are based were done with *E. coli*. Bollum and Potter[18] have worked with a variety of animal tissues and have found DNA polymerase in regenerating rat liver and many other tissues from the rat, as well as nuclei from the thymus gland of the calf. This is a very convenient source of metabolically active nuclei. The polymerase from calf thymus requires denatured DNA but also has the characteristic of being primed by rather small oligo deoxynucleotides.

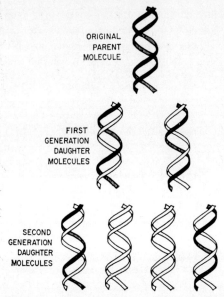

FIG. 4.4. Semi-conservative replication of DNA. In conservative replication the two original chains never come apart. In semi-conservative replication they separate and a hybrid is formed consisting of one old and one new chain. (Figure based on Meselson and Stahl but from F. H. C. Crick, *Proc. VIth Int. Congress of Biochemistry*, New York, 1964, p. 109.)

RNA synthesis

So far as we are concerned the structure of RNA only differs from that of DNA in the presence of ribose instead of deoxyribose and the substitution of uracil for thymine (see Fig. 4.1). It has been known for a long time that if a cell is presented with an RNA precursor such as radioactive phosphorus, the nuclear RNA is metabolically more active than the cytoplasmic RNA. Thus, long before the discovery of m-RNA, it was suspected that the cytoplasmic RNA was derived from the nucleus.

In Chapter 3 we described briefly the way in which m-RNA transfers the information contained within the base sequence of DNA to the site of protein synthesis—the ribosomes—in the cytoplasm. The precise extent to which all the RNA synthesis of the nucleus is directed to the synthesis of m-RNA is disputed. The original experiments on m-RNA and much of the more recent work was done with bacteria, which, of course, have no nucleus. Harris,[19] of Oxford, and Darnell,[20] in Boston, have worked with HeLa cells which are derived from a human tumour. It seems that in such cells much of the RNA that is synthesized in the nucleus is also broken down there and does not reach the cytoplasm. Although most people now accept that some nuclear RNA does reach the cytoplasm, it has been difficult to obtain clear cut evidence for the action of m-RNA in nucleated animal cells. In reticulocytes Arnstein[21] has shown that an extract of RNA will cause an otherwise inactive fraction of ribosomes to synthesize haemoglobin.

The way in which RNA is synthesized was discovered independently by two Americans. Weiss[22] who showed the presence in extracts of rat liver homogenate of an enzyme called RNA polymerase, and Hurwitz[23] who demonstrated the same enzyme in *E. coli*. The general characteristics of this enzyme are similar to those of the DNA polymerase of Kornberg, the main difference being that RNA and not DNA is produced using the ribo- in place of the deoxyribo-nucleoside triphosphates. DNA serves as the template primer and in this case the RNA synthesized has a base composition close to that of the priming DNA, except that uracil takes the place of thymine. The yield of RNA can be many times greater than the amount of DNA template used. Both double-stranded and single stranded DNA can serve as primer but native DNA is the more effective. When duplex DNA is primer the strands are not first separated. This is different from the case for DNA synthesis where the strands separate in order to act as a template. Under *in vitro* conditions both strands of DNA serve as templates but *in vivo* it appears that only one is used. Weiss has shown that the polymerase is located specifically in the nucleus of the rat liver cell.

RNA polymerase can also utilize RNA itself as primer. We do not know the full significance of this in the cell although we do know that some such reaction must sometimes occur as when an RNA virus infects a cell. Under these conditions the RNA of the virus primes the polymerase for the synthesis of more viral RNA.[24] Subsequently, the viral RNA serves as its own m-RNA and short circuits the usual step involving DNA for the synthesis of viral protein.

Spiegelman and Hall[25] at the University of Illinois have made remarkable use of a technique known as hybridization. We have already explained that when DNA is heated the strands separate. If this is done carefully and the rate of cooling also controlled, the two strands will reassociate provided the ionic composition of the medium is suitable. If this treatment is applied to a mixture of DNA and RNA, then, if the RNA has a base sequence that is complementary to that of DNA over a large stretch, the RNA will form a duplex with one strand of the DNA so that a DNA/RNA hybrid is formed. This method can be used as a test of the "complementarity" of the DNA and RNA. Moreover, when the RNA is hybridized with DNA it is no longer susceptible to the action of ribonuclease which can, therefore, be used as a test of hydrid formation. In this way Spiegelman has shown that both ribosomal RNA and S-RNA in *E. coli* are synthesized on a DNA template. We can, therefore, say that all three kinds of RNA are made on a DNA template and this is indicated in the summary figure in Chapter 3 (Fig. 3.6).

The interesting effects of the anti-tumour agent actinomycin D may now be considered. The mechanism of action of this substance has been studied by many workers, notably the Americans, Rabinowitz and Reich.[26] Actinomycin inhibits both DNA and RNA polymerases *in vitro* but the RNA enzyme is much more sensitive than the DNA enzyme. Thus at low concentration *in vivo* it is virtually a specific inhibitor of the RNA polymerase which utilizes DNA as primer for the synthesis of m-RNA. The reason that it is specific for the DNA primed enzyme is that it combines with deoxyguanosine which, of course, only occurs in DNA. It is not clear why it should be more effective with the RNA polymerase than the DNA enzyme but there is some evidence that this is because the former enzyme requires native DNA as primer in contrast to the denatured DNA required for the latter.

Actinomycin has the effect of blocking protein synthesis only when such synthesis depends on a supply of fresh m-RNA. Where the synthesis is performed in the presence of stable m-RNA, protein synthesis is not affected by actinomycin. Hence the effect of this substance is often to cause an increase in the proportion of monomeric ribosomes to polysomes, since there is a shortage of m-RNA to link the ribosomes together. The results are more clear cut in bacteria than in a system such as rat liver where it has been shown that actinomycin has certain confusing effects which are little understood.[27] In spite of this, actinomycin has found a wide use to determine whether under certain conditions, for example the administration of a hormone such as thyroxine,[28] the synthesis of m-RNA has been stimulated or whether the effect of the hormone has merely been to increase the rate of protein synthesis utilizing existing m-RNA.

Finally, we should mention that the Swedish biochemist Reichard[29] has shown that, in the formation of DNA, ribonucleotides are converted to deoxyribonucleotides so that the change in the sugar moiety takes place at the nucleotide level. Reference to Fig. 3.6 will show this reaction in the general scheme.

Metabolism of Nucleic Acids—Morphological Aspects

The most direct test for the effect of the nucleus on the nucleic acid metabolism of the cell is to tranfer a nucleus from a normal cell to an enucleated cell and to determine the metabolism of the cell with its newly won nucleus. It is naturally difficult to ensure that under these conditions some of the cytoplasm is not transplanted with the nucleus. A good example of the use of such a technique is that described by Gurdon of Oxford in collaboration with Brown of Baltimore.[30]

Gurdon and Brown worked with *Xenopus laevis*, the larval form of the South African "clawed toad". When a cell nucleus is transplanted from an embryo or tadpole into an enucleated unfertilized egg, the transplanted nucleus substitutes functionally for the zygote nucleus and promotes normal embryonic development in thirty to forty per cent of the cases. The object then was to determine whether the functional changes which such a transplanted nucleus undergoes are accompanied by modification of the pattern of RNA synthesis which the transplanted nucleus and its descendants support. The experiment depended on the fact that the nucleus was transplanted from a tissue which was actively and predominantly synthesizing ribosomal RNA. The object, therefore, was to determine whether the resulting nuclear-transplant embryo retained the pattern of RNA synthesis characteristic of the more differentiated donor tissue or whether the synthetic pattern reverted to that of a normal embryo derived from a fertilized egg. The results of the experiment showed that after transplantation the nuclear-transplant embryo had a pattern of RNA synthesis which was indistinguishable from that of normal embryos derived from fertilized eggs. The embryos synthesized messenger like RNA and S-RNA but no ribosomal-RNA. Thus the synthesis of RNA in the nucleus is regulated by the type of cytoplasm in which the nucleus lies.

Another experiment with $X.$ $laevis$ by Brown and Gurdon[31] is of particular interest in deciding the role of nucleoli in ribosomal synthesis. They worked on two different observations. The first concerns the fact that few ribosomes appear in the cytoplasm of their embryonic cells before a certain stage in their development. At this stage the number of such ribosomes begins to increase and the embryos develop a requirement for Mg^{2+} ions in the medium. Without magnesium the embryos stop growing and die. Thus the magnesium requirement coincides with the onset of intense ribosome synthesis, and from what we have already learnt about ribosome structure this is not surprising.

The second observation concerns the mutant of $Xenopus$ which Elsdale first described and which has no nucleoli. There is also a heterozygote mutant with only one nucleolus in each cell whereas the wild type has two in the majority of their diploid cells. If the two heterozygotes were mated, three groups arose as expected; 2-nu, 1-nu or 0-nu having 2, 1 or no nucleoli per cell. The 0-nu mutant has numerous small nucleolar blobs instead of nucleoli. The development of these embryos is retarded shortly after hatching and they show characteristics very similar to embryos suffering from magnesium deficiency. Thus it was thought possible that the 0-nu mutants might be incapable of synthesizing ribosomes and ribosomal RNA. They found in fact that no 28S or 18S ribosomal RNA was synthesized but that DNA and two types of RNA, which appeared to be S-RNA and m-RNA, were synthesized by the 0-nu. The 0-nu show normal differentiation of all the main cell types despite their inability to synthesize new ribosomal RNA. 0-nu conserved the ribosomes which had been previously made during oogenesis and the newly synthesized m-RNA associated with these old ribosomes.

Gurdon and Brown also found that the base ratios of the 28S and 18S ribosomal RNA differed and that they were probably, therefore, products of different genes although their synthesis was co-ordinated. In the heterozygous 1-nu embryo the wild-type genes control the production of twice as much 28S as 18S ribosomal RNA as do the same genes in the homozygous wild-type individual. Since the activity of the entire complement of genes determining ribosomal RNA structure can be curtailed by a single mutation, it is suggested that these genes are under common control and are located at the nucleolar site of a single chromosome.

Two other methods of determining the role of the nucleolus must be mentioned. In the first, Perry[32] has irradiated the nucleolus of HeLa cells with a microbeam of ultraviolet light. In this way he abolished virtually all incorporation of the precursors into the RNA of the nucleolus and the subsequent accumulation of RNA in the cytoplasm was reduced by 70%. The microbeam irradiation of non-nucleolar parts of the nucleus was without effect. This evidence supports the idea that ribosomal RNA is derived from the nucleolus.

The other method is that of microdissection used by Edström of Gothenburg, Sweden. He first used spider oocytes,[33] removed the nucleoli by micromanipulation and determined the base ratios of the RNA. He found that the ratios of the nucleolar RNA and ribosomal RNA matched rather well whereas the nucleoplasmic RNA was quite different and bore more resemblance to DNA. Later he used *Asterias rubens* oocytes and came to a similar conclusion.

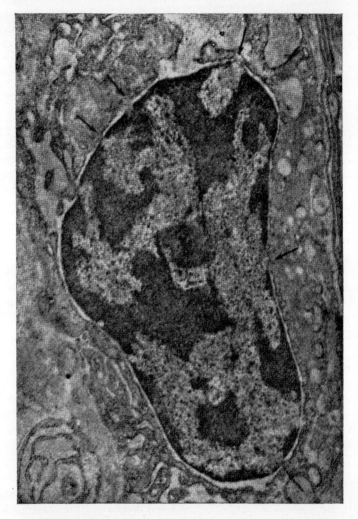

PLATE IV.4. Portion of a mucous epithelium cell from the Anolis lizard. The fixation method used does not reveal the membranous components of the cytoplasm but it can be seen that the perinuclear space is continuous with the lumen of expanded cisternae of rough surfaced endoplasmic reticulum. The cytoplasm around the

Busch[34] has studied extensively the synthesis of nucleolar and extranucleolar RNA in the nucleus of normal and tumour cells and has concluded that the two types of RNA are synthesized independently. As if to reinforce the projected role of the nucleolus in the synthesis of ribosomal RNA, Birnstiel,[35] working in California, has detected ribosomal-like particles in the nucleolus and it is tempting to conclude that they are assembled there.

There has been much discussion as to whether RNA synthesis is entirely confined to the nucleus or whether some goes on in the cytoplasm.[36] It is clear that certain nucleotides are built into RNA in the cytoplasm, such as the terminal three nucleotides in S-RNA,[37] but perhaps it is better to regard such synthesis in terms of repair rather than *de novo* synthesis of nucleic acid. The conclusion at present is that no *de novo* synthesis of RNA takes place in the cytoplasm.

The m-RNA hypothesis predicts that in a nucleated cell the RNA will be synthesized in the nucleus and moves to the cytoplasm where it will become associated with the ribosomes. This scheme certainly poses a number of questions in morphology. Watson[38] was the first to demonstrate that in the liver cell the nuclear envelope is continuous with the rough endoplasmic reticulum. A very nice illustration of this is shown in Plate IV.4 which is an electron micrograph of a mucous cell from the lizard ureter. Here the outer of the two membranes of the envelope of the nucleus is enlarged to form the reticulum. Both here and in the electron micrographs of the liver nucleus (Plate IV.2) the pores appear to pass through both the membranes of the envelope. Thus if m-RNA were to leave the nucleus through the pores, it is theoretically possible for it to reach the ribosomes attached to the rough endoplasmic reticulum. Although, therefore, the arrangements are satisfactory for the passage of m-RNA from the nucleus to the ribosomes, one must wonder

endoplasmic reticulum is in contact with the nucleus through pores (*arrows*) in the perinuclear envelope. Magnification × 22,000. (Electron micrograph by courtesy of R. M. Hicks, Bland Sutton Institute of Pathology, The Middlesex Hospital.)

how this material survives the passage in view of its easy susceptibility to nucleases. Moreover, the build-up of the polysomes on
the membrane must be a very complex business. In view of the
continuity of the rough endoplasmic reticulum and the nuclear
membranes one wonders whether the assembly point is not the
nuclear membranes themselves which then stream off to form the
rough endoplasmic reticulum. This, however, is sheer conjecture
for we do not yet know definitely where the ribosomes are assembled
nor the metabolic state of activity of the nuclear membranes.

Other Metabolic Activities of the Nucleus

As Roodyn has pointed out, any consideration of the use of
single enzymes for assessing the activity of isolated nuclei leads
to only one enzyme, namely NAD-pyrophosphorylase. This is the
only enzyme so far discovered that is highly concentrated in a
nuclear fraction and which is essentially absent from all other
cell fractions. Table 4.1 is a summary prepared by Roodyn of
biochemical processes observed in isolated rat or mouse liver nuclear
fractions.

Although the nucleus is unique in its biochemical activity concerning the nucleic acids, in other repsects it seems to be able to
perform most of the metabolic reactions of the cytoplasm, even
though at a lower level of activity. Mirsky and Allfrey,[39] and their
colleagues of the Rockefeller Institute, New York, have made a
very extensive study of the protein synthesizing activity of nuclei
both from liver and calf thymus. They conclude that such nuclear
preparations are able to perform all the reactions involved in the
synthesis of protein. The most notable difference between the
nuclear and cytoplasmic reactions is the requirement for the latter
of K^+ ions and of the former for Na^+ ions. This may be because
of a specific Na^+ ion requirement for the transport of amino acids
into the nucleus.

One of the best ways of assessing the activity of the nucleus in the
metabolism of the cell as a whole is to remove it and study the activity
of the anucleate cell. Some of the most convincing experiments

TABLE 4.1. VARIOUS BIOCHEMICAL REACTIONS OBSERVED IN NUCLEAR
FRACTIONS FROM RAT OR MOUSE LIVER

Isolation medium	Reference	Reaction observed
Organic solvents	Siebert (1961)	Total glycolysis and numerous glycolytic enzymes
—	Shonk and Boxer (1957)	Glyceraldehyde-3-phos + acetaldehyde → deoxyribose-5-phos
0·25 M Sucrose	Preiss and Handler (1958)	Desamido NMN + ATP desamido NAD + P–P
0·25 M Sucrose	Schneider (1959)	Transfer of *in vivo* labelled nuclear RNA to cytoplasmic fractions on *in vitro* incubation
0·25 M Sucrose	Logan and Smellie (1956)	Transfer of *in vivo* ^{32}P-labelled cytoplasmic material to nuclear RNA on *in vitro* incubation
Sucrose–CaCl$_2$	Maley, Maley and Lardy (1956)	UTP + glucosamine-1-phos → UDP glucosamine
Sucrose–CaCl$_2$	Smith, Munch-Peterson and Mills (1953)	UDPG + P–P→UTP
Sucrose–CaCl$_2$	Hogeboom and Schneider (1952*b*) Branster and Morton (1956)(M)	NMN + ATP ⇌ NAD + P–P
Sucrose–CaCl$_2$	Stirpe and Aldridge (1961)	NMN + ATP ⇌ NAD + P–P
Sucrose–CaCl$_2$	Logan, Ficq and Errera (1959)	*In vitro* incorporation of ^{14}C-phenylalanine and adenine into nuclei (autoradiography)
Sucrose–CaCl$_2$	Rees and Rowland (1961)	*In vitro* incorporation of ^{14}C-glycine into protein and ^{14}C-adenine and orotic acid into RNA
Sucrose–CaCl$_2$	Rendi (1960)	*In vitro* incorporation of several ^{14}C-amino acids into protein

[*Table continued*]

TABLE 4.1.—*continued*

Isolation medium	Reference	Reaction observed
2·2 M Sucrose	Rendi (1960)	*In vitro* incorporation of several ^{14}C-amino acids into protein
2·2 M Sucrose–CaCl$_2$	Gvosdev (1960)	Tyrosine activating enzyme
0·25 M Sucrose–MgCl$_2$	Weiss (1960)	*In vitro* incorporation of ^{32}P-nucleoside triphosphates into RNA

using this method were done by Hämmerling[40] with the green alga *Acetabularia*. He showed that in this organism the synthesis of specific proteins could continue for many weeks after the removal of the nucleus. In the case of the *Amoeba*, where it is possible to cut the cell into two parts, the anucleate part, although capable of protein synthesis, only had half the activity of the nucleate part. This work was done by Brachet,[41] and his colleagues in Brussels. Studies on non-nucleate fragments of sea urchin eggs or of newt eggs also showed that various labelled protein precursors can be incorporated into proteins in a cytoplasm without a nucleus.[42] There is also the rabbit reticulocyte which contains no nucleus but makes perfectly normal haemoglobin. The conclusion from all these experiments is that the cytoplasm is capable of synthesizing protein by itself but that the length of time it can continue to do this without a nucleus depends on the metabolic stability of m-RNA.

Nature and Function of Nuclear Proteins

We have already stated that isolated liver nuclei contain as much as 75% protein so that it is right that we should consider briefly the nature and function of these proteins. The nuclear proteins are basic and are linked to DNA by ionic forces between the phosphate groups of the nucleic acid and the basic amino acid residues of the proteins.

The nuclear proteins are of two kinds. The histones, which are of general occurrence in all animal tissues, have a high molecular weight and are rich in arginine or lysine or both, but deficient in tryptophan. The protamines are only found in the ripe sperm of certain families of fish and never in somatic cell nuclei. They are very basic and are relatively small proteins lacking many amino acids but very rich in arginine.

A great deal of work has been done in an attempt to subfractionate the histones, especially those in calf thymus nuclei, and Butler and his group in London have been particularly active in this respect. They have separated the histones into three main groups by column chromatography, obtaining lysine-rich histones, slightly lysine-rich histones and arginine-rich histones. The second group can be further subdivided to give four groups in all.[43] When the histones from different tissues of the same or widely different animals are compared, few qualitative differences are found, although there may be quantitative variations as between the different groups.[44]

In 1950 Stedman,[45] and his wife, working in Edinburgh, suggested that histones might control gene function. As we have previously mentioned all the cells of a particular animal contain the same DNA but as a result of differentiation the various types of cell utilize different pieces of information (genes). Hence, some parts of the DNA in a particular cell must be rendered ineffectual or some of the m-RNA made from the entire DNA molecule must be broken down selectively before it can become effective as a template for protein synthesis. The mechanisms whereby genetic information is controlled in bacteria have been elegantly worked out by Monod,[46] and his school at the Institut Pasteur in Paris. They have shown that a metabolite combines with a repressor which is made by a regulatory gene. Since bacteria do not contain histones these experiments tell us nothing directly about the role of these proteins in animal cells. An encouraging start was made when Bonner,[47] and his colleagues in California showed that whereas DNA from pea seedlings served as a primer for DNA polymerase, when it was complexed with histone, in amounts approaching those present in the native complex, its primer activity was markedly reduced. This experiment has been confirmed with extracts from other tissues.

If histones really do act as gene regulators, then Butler argues that we should be able to show a differential effect on the DNA as between histones of different composition and character. This effect could either be studied by following the DNA polymerase reaction or by studying the chemical interaction between DNA and histone fractions. So far neither approach has yielded results which clearly implicate histones as gene regulators but the idea remains a possibility.[48]

References

1. A. E. MIRSKY and S. OSAWA, The interphase nucleus, *The Cell* (Ed. BRACHET and MIRSKY), Vol. 2, p. 677, Academic Press, New York, 1961.
2. C. A. STONEBURG, Lipids in the cell nuclei, *J. biol. Chem.*, **129**, 189–96 (1963).
3. J. CHAUVEAU, Y. MOULÉ, and C. ROUILLER, Isolation of pure and unaltered liver nuclei. Morphology and biochemical composition, *Exp. Cell Res.*, **11**, 317–21 (1956).
4. R. MAGGIO, P. SIEKEVITZ and G. E. PALADE, Studies on isolated nuclei I, *J. Cell Biol.*, **18**, 267–91 (1963).
5. C. C. WIDNELL and J. R. TATA, A procedure for the isolation of enzymically active rat-liver nuclei, *Biochem. J.*, **92**, 313–17 (1964).
6. M. B. SPORN, T. WANKO and W. DINGMAN, The isolation of cell nuclei from rat brain, *J. Cell Biol.*, **15**, 109–20 (1962).
7. R. MAGGIO, P. SIEKEVITZ and G. E. PALADE, Studies on isolated nuclei II, *J. Cell Biol.*, **18**, 293–312 (1963).
8. J. D. WATSON and F. H. C. CRICK, Molecular structure of nuclei acids: a structure for deoxypentose nucleic acids, *Nature, Lond.*, **171**, 737–8 (1953).
9. R. L. SINSHEIMER, A single-stranded deoxyribonucleic acid from bacteriophage Φ x 174, *J. molec. Biol.*, **1**, 43–53 (1959).
10. I. R. LEHMANN, M. J. BESSMAN, E. S. SIMMS and A. KORNBERG, Enzymatic synthesis of deoxyribonucleic acid I, *J. biol. Chem.*, **233**, 163–70 (1958); M. J. BESSMAN, I. R. LEHMANN, E. S. SIMMS and A. KORNBERG, Enzymatic synthesis of deoxyribonucleic acid II, *J. biol. Chem.*, **233**, 171–7 (1958); A. KORNBERG, Enzymatic synthesis of DNA, *CIBA Lectures on Microbial Biochemistry*, p. 14, Wiley, New York, 1961.
11. J. JOSSE, A. D. KAISER and A. KORNBERG, Enzymatic synthesis of deoxyribonucleic acid VIII, *J. biol. Chem.*, **236**, 864–75 (1961).
12. M. MESELSON and F. W. STAHL, The replication of DNA in *Escherichia coli*, *Proc. nat. Acad. Sci. Wash.*, **44**, 671 (1958).

13. E. H. L. CHUN and J. W. LITTLEFIELD, The separation of the light and heavy strands of bromouracil substituted mammalian DNA, *J. molec. Biol.*, **3**, 668–73 (1961).

14. J. H. TAYLOR, P. S. WOODS and W. L. HUGHES, The organization and duplication of chromosomes as revealed by autoradiographic studies using titrium labeled thymidine, *Proc. nat. Acad. Sci. Wash.*, **43**, 122–8 (1957); J. H. TAYLOR, in *Molecular Genetics*, Part I (Ed. J. H. TAYLOR), p. 65, Academic Press, New York, 1963.

15. J. CAIRNS, The bacterial chromosome and its manner of replication as seen by autoradiography, *J. molec. Biol.* **6**, 208–13 (1963).

16. R. DULBECCO, Configurational and biological properties of polyoma virus DNA, *Proc. roy. Soc.*, 1964, **160B**, 423–31 (1964).

17. F. H. C. CRICK, The biochemistry of genetics, *Proc. 6th Int. Congr. Biochem., New York*, 109–28 (1964).

18. F. J. BOLLUM and V. R. POTTER, Incorporation of thymidine into deoxyribonucleic acid by enzymes from rat tissues, *J. biol. Chem.*, **233**, 478–82 (1958); F. J. BOLLUM, Primer in DNA polymerase reactions, *Progr. Nucleic Acid Res.*, **1**, 1–26 (1963).

19. H. HARRIS, Nuclear ribonucleic acid, *Progr. Nucleic Acid Res.*, **2**, 19–59 (1963).

20. M. GIRARD, H. LATHAM, S. PENMAN and J. E. DARNELL, Entrance of newly formed messenger RNA and ribosomes into HeLa cell cytoplasm, *J. molec. Biol.*, **11**, 187–201 (1965).

21. H. R. V. ARNSTEIN, R. A. COX and J. A. HUNT, The function of high molecular weight ribonucleic acid from rabbit reticulocytes in haemoglobin biosynthesis, *Biochem. J.*, **92**, 648–61 (1964).

22. S. B. WEISS, Enzymatic incorporation of ribonucleoside triphosphates into the interpolynucleotide linkages of ribonucleic acid, *Proc. nat. Acad. Sci. Wash.*, **6**, 1020–30 (1960).

23. J. HURWITZ, A. BRESLER and R. DIRINGER, The enzymic incorporation of ribonucleotides into polyribonucleotides and the effect of DNA, *Biochem. biophys. Res. Comm.*, **3**, 15–19 (1960); J. HURWITZ and J. T. AUGUST, The role of DNA in RNA synthesis, *Progr. Nucleic Acid Res.*, **1**, 59–92 (1963).

24. P. J. GOMATOS, R. M. KRUG, and I. TAMM, Enzymic synthesis of RNA with reovirus RNA as template, *J. molec. Biol.*, **9**, 193–207 (1964).

25. B. D. HALL and S. SPIEGELMAN, Sequence complementarity of T2-DNA and T2-Specific RNA, *Proc. nat. Acad. Sci. Wash.*, **47**, 137–46 (1961); S. SPIEGELMAN and M. HAYASHI, The present status of the transfer of genetic information and its control, *Cold Spring Harbor Symp. Quant. Biol.*, **28**, 161–81 (1963).

26. E. REICH, R. M. FRANKLIN, A. J. SHATKIN and E. L. TATUM, Effect of actinomycin D on cellular nucleic acid synthesis and virus production, *Science*, **134**, 556–7 (1961); I. H. GOLDBERG, M. RABINOWITZ and E. REICH, Basis of actinomycin action I, *Proc. nat. Acad. Sci. Wash.*, **48**, 2094–101 (1962); E. REICH and I. H. GOLDBERG, Actinomycin and nucleic acid function, *Progr. Nucleic Acid Res.*, **3**, 183–234 (1964).

27. M. Revel, H. H. Hiatt and J. P. Revel, Actinomycin D. An effect on rat liver homogenates unrelated to its action on RNA synthesis, *Science*, **146**, 1311–3 (1964).

28. J. R. Tata, Inhibition of the biological action of thyroid hormones by actinomycin D and puromycin, *Nature, Lond.*, **197**, 1167–8 (1963).

29. P. Reichard, Formation of deoxyguanosine 5'-phosphate from guanosine 5'-phosphate with enzymes from chick embryos, *Biochim. biophys. Acta*, **41**, 368–9 (1960); P. Reichard, Enzymic formation of deoxyribonucleic acid from ribonucleotides, *Biological structure and Function*, Vol. I (Ed. Goodwin and Lindberg), p. 103, Academic Press, London, 1961.

30. J. B. Gurdon and D. D. Brown, Cytoplasmic regulation of RNA synthesis and nucleolus formation in developing embryos of *Xenopus laevis*, *J. molec. Biol.*, **12**, 27–35 (1965).

31. D. D. Brown and J. B. Gurdon, Absence of ribosomal RNA synthesis in the anucleolate mutant of *Xenopus laevis*, *Proc. nat. Acad. Sci. Wash.*, **51**, 139–46 (1964).

32. R. P. Perry, A. Hell and M. Errera, The role of the nucleolus in ribonucleic acid and protein synthesis, *Biochim. biophys. Acta*, **49**, 47–57 (1961).

33. J-E. Edström, Composition of ribonucleic acid from various parts of spider oocytes, *J. biophys. biochem. Cytol.*, **8**, 47–51 (1960); J-E. Edström, W. Grampp and N. Schor, The intracellular distribution and heterogeneity of ribonucleic acids in Starfish oocytes, *J. biophys. biochem. Cytol.*, **11**, 549–57 (1961).

34. M. Muramatsu, J. L. Hodnett and H. Busch, Studies on the independence of nucleolar ribonucleic acid synthesis, *Biochim. biophys. Acta*, **91**, 592–7 (1964).

35. M. L. Birnstiel, M. I. H. Chipchase and B. B. Hyde, The nucleolus, a source of ribosomes, *Biochim. biophys. Acta*, **76**, 454–62 (1963).

36. D. M. Prescott, Cellular sites of RNA synthesis, *Progr. Nucleic Acid. Res.*, **3**, 33–57 (1964).

37. L. I. Hecht, M. L. Stephenson and P. C. Zamecnik, Binding of amino acids to the end group of a soluble ribonucleic acid, *Proc. nat. Acad. Sci. Wash.*, **45**, 505–18 (1959).

38. M. L. Watson, The nuclear envelope. Its structure and relation to cytoplasmic membranes, *J. biophys. biochem. Cytol.*, **1**, 257–70 (1955).

39. V. G. Allfrey, A. E. Mirsky and S. Osawa, Protein synthesis in isolated cell nuclei, *J. gen. Physiol.*, **40**, 451–90 (1957).

40. J. von Hämmerling, Nucleocytoplasmic relationships in the development of Acetabularia, *Int. Rev. Cytol.*, **2**, 475–98 (1953).

41. J. Brachet, Recherches sur les interactions biochimiques entre le noyau et le cytoplasme chez les organisms unicellularies, *Biochim. biophys. Acta*, **18**, 247–68 (1955).

42. H. M. Malkin, Synthesis of ribonucleic acid purines and protein in enucleated and nucleated sea urchin eggs, *J. cell. comp. Physiol.*, **44**, 105–12 (1954).

43. E. W. JOHNS, Studies on histones, *Biochem. J.*, **92**, 55–9 (1964).
44. L. HNILICA, E. W. JOHNS and J. A. V. BUTLER, Observations on the species and tissue specificity of histones, *Biochem. J.*, 123–9 (1962).
45. E. STEDMAN and E. STEDMAN, Cell specificity of histones, *Nature, Lond.*, **166**, 780–1 (1950).
46. J. MONOD, J. P. CHANGEUX and F. JACOB, Allosteric proteins and cellular control systems, *J. molec. Biol.*, **6**, 306–29 (1963); J. P. CHANGEUX, The control of biochemical reactions, *Scientific American*, p. 36, April, 1965.
47. R. C. HUANG and J. BONNER, Histone, a suppressor of chromosomal RNA synthesis, *Proc. nat. Acad. Sci. Wash.*, **48**, 1216–22 (1962).
48. E. W. JOHNS and J. A. V. BUTLER, Specificity of the interaction between histones and deoxyribonucleic acid, *Nature, Lond.*, **204**, 853–5 (1964).

Further Reading

S. SPIEGELMAN, Hybrid nucleic acids, *Scientific American*, p. 48, May 1964.
D. B. ROODYN, A comparative account of methods for the isolation of nuclei, *Biochem. Soc. Symp.*, **23**, 20 (1963).
M. F. PERUTZ, *Proteins and Nucleic Acids*, Elsevier, Amsterdam, 1962; Synthesis and structure of macromolecules, *Cold Harbor Symp. Quant. Biol.*, **28**, (1963).
J. N. DAVIDSON, *The Biochemistry of the Nucleic Acids*, Methuen, London, 5th Ed. 1965.
J. D. ROBERTSON, The membrane of the living cell, *Scientific American*, p. 64, April 1962.

F

CHAPTER 5

Lysosomes and the Breakdown of Extraneous Biological Substances

So FAR in this book we have been considering the structure and function of more or less "permanent" organelles. Now we turn to some that are less permanent and which play an important role in the internal digestion of the cell. Most cells are able to assimilate substances and objects which are too big to pass through the molecular mesh which comprises the cell membrane. They do this by a process of pinocytosis or phagocytosis. The former term was coined by Warren Lewis in 1931[1] to describe the process of active drinking by cells. As Holter[2] of Copenhagen has said, "there is no sharp distinction between pinocytosis and phagocytosis, since the main difference seems not to be the mechanism of the process but rather the dimensions involved and the nature of the ingested material". De Duve, the Belgian biochemist, has suggested the combined term "endocytosis",[3] but this has not yet found universal application.

The result of pinocytosis is, of course, the presence in the cytoplasm of a vesicle or vacuole. Similarly, when a cell wishes to rid itself of some substance or material a vacuole is formed which, as we shall see, may be called a residual body. In addition to these organelles de Duve and his group from Louvain characterized another organelle and named it the "lysosome" or "lytic body" in 1955.[4] The subject of this chapter is, therefore, the way in which we believe lysosomes play their part in the phenomenon of pinocytosis. I plan to first describe how de Duve and his colleagues came to discover the properties of the lysosomes, then to describe a few classical examples of pinocytosis and finally to see how the whole scheme can be fitted together.

The Isolation of and Properties of Lysosomes and Microbodies

De Duve's work sprang from a chance observation in 1949.[5] He was using the technique of differential centrifugation to determine the distribution of the enzymes involved in the metabolism of carbohydrate among the different fractions. As a control he also assayed for the activity of the acid phosphatase which plays no role in carbohydrate metabolism but for which β-glycerophosphate is usually used as a substrate. He found that liver tissue which was freshly homogenized in isotonic sucrose had much less acid phosphatase activity than the same tissue homogenized in distilled water. If the particulate fractions were isolated, they also had low enzyme activity but when the preparations were allowed to age the enzyme activity greatly increased. Whereas the enzyme was largely present in the particulate fraction isolated from the fresh homogenate, it no longer sedimented from the aged preparations. Thus, he argued, the enzyme must be present in a particle the membrane of which could be disrupted. From this observation he set out to identify the particles involved.

De Duve has stated that his exploration was based on two premises which are interesting to us since they have general application. The first is the concept of biochemical homogeneity, that is to say that all members of a given subcellular population have the same enzymic composition. One can think of the mitochondria as being the supreme and perhaps only example of this principle, for the enzymic composition of mitochondria does not vary with their size. The second premise is that of single location, that is to say that each enzyme is entirely restricted to a single site within the cell. Examples of this of this are glucose 6-phosphatase which, as we have seen, is located in the endoplasmic reticulum, and cytochrome oxidase which is only found in the mitochondria. (The fact that some enzymes are found both in the mitochondria and in the so-called soluble fraction is against this premise but there are special considerations in this case.)

It was on the above premises that de Duve based his ultracentrifugal techniques aimed at the location of acid phosphatase. The ultracentrifuge can be regarded as both a preparative and an analytical instrument whereby it is possible to ascertain some of the physical properties of the substances or particles isolated. Two general methods of differential centrifugation in density gradients may be used. These have briefly been described in Chapter 1 and reference to Fig. 1.4. will be useful. In the first technique it is essential to layer the starting material on top of a stabilizing gradient and then centrifuge in a centrifugal field which is not great enough to cause the complete sedimentation of even the heaviest component. As shown in Fig. 1.4. at the end of the run the position of the different components will depend on their sedimentation coefficients. In this case the density gradient serves only a stabilizing purpose, its slope is usually small and its upper limit is lower than the density of any of the components, so that if the centrifugation went on long enough all the material would arrive at the bottom of the tube.

In the second technique the starting material can be placed either at the top of the tube or some way down. The density gradient is usually much steeper and the upper limit is above the density of the heaviest component. Spinning is prolonged so that the particles are fully separated and reach a position in the gradient corresponding to their own density. This is known as the isopycnic method or density equilibration. In general the first technique is used for both preparative and analytical purposes and the second for analytical purposes.

If in either of the above methods fractions are taken from along the gradient at the end of the centrifugation and the concentration of enzyme determined in each fraction, a frequency distribution curve is obtained. If the distribution curve for two enzymes differs significantly, it can be concluded that they are located in different particles. If they coincide, then it is an indication that they may be associated with the same type of particle.

When the distribution of acid phosphatase was studied by the above methods it was found that it had a broad distribution between mitochondria and microsomes. It appeared, therefore, that this enzyme was associated with a new type of particle. The methods were then used to determine the distribution curve for other enzymes and so far at least fifteen have been studied. When the fractions were subjected to density equilibration in various gradients containing different materials, it was found that the enzymes separated into two subgroups, one containing all the acid hydrolases and the other including urate oxidase, catalase and D-amino acid oxidase. The results are summarized in Fig. 5.1. De Duve and his colleagues

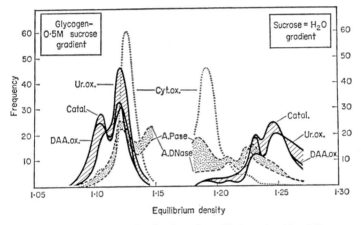

FIG. 5.1. Frequency distribution of equilibrium densities. Mitochondrial fractions from rat liver equilibrated in a gradient of glycogen in 0·5 M sucrose and in a linear gradient of sucrose. (From C. de Duve, ref. 5.)

concluded from these results that two different kinds of organelle were involved. The one, later identified as the microbodies, containing the three enzymes, and the other, by lysosomes, containing the hydrolytic enzymes. From the frequency distribution curves the microbodies could be a homogeneous group, i.e. each particle containing all three enzymes although, as shown in Fig. 5.1, amino acid oxidase and catalase are easily released whereas urate oxidase is firmly attached. The lysosomes are characterized by a fair degree of heterogeneity both with respect to size, stability and enzyme composition. Another way of demonstrating the presence of two kinds of organelle is to inject a rat with the synthetic detergent,

Triton. The density of the lysosomes is changed as a result of their taking up the detergent but the density of the other particles including the microbodies is not affected. Fractions rich in either microbodies or lysosomes have now been examined by electron microscopy and shown to differ markedly in appearance.[6]

From the morphological viewpoint Porter[7] of Boston summarizes the position as follows. The microbodies in their mature fully developed form vary in size from $0.4\ \mu$ to $1\ \mu$, are partly round in outline, surrounded by a single membrane and exhibit a matrix of moderate density which appears amorphous or finely granular. One of the most distinctive features of the microbodies is a dense core or nucleoid, often exhibiting a highly organized structure which may be urate oxidase. Lysosomes differ from microbodies in having a denser matrix and the presence of droplets or vacuoles. They have two common features, a dense core and a denser peripheral rim. The microbodies have some features in common with the zymogen granules of the pancreas but it may be noted that while the enzymes of the microbodies are for the internal activity of the cell those within the zymogen granules are for export.

We mentioned in Chapter 1 the use of histochemical techniques to determine the localization of enzymes in section of cells and that this technique was particularly useful for hydrolytic enzymes. Novikoff,[8] of the Albert Einstein College of Medicine in New York, and Holt,[9] in London, have, therefore, used these cytochemical methods to identify the lysosomes in tissue sections. Many of the conclusions of de Duve on the stability of lysosomes have been confirmed in this way and, moreover, it has been shown that the particles are indeed heterogeneous, some staining for the presence of one enzyme and some for another. At the electron microscope level the phosphate released by the action of acid phosphatase is coupled to lead and the insoluble lead phosphate detected in electron micrographs.[10] This method has greatly facilitated the identification and study of lysosomes and their function in numerous tissues, both normal and pathological.

We have already mentioned that acid phosphatase appears not to be active when associated with the particles in a homogenate but can be released in an active form. This is known as "latency" and it is a common feature of all the fifteen enzymes now known to be associated with the lysosomes. The idea is that the enzymes, all of which are potentially dangerous to the cell since they are hydrolases, are perfectly active within the lysosome but the lipoprotein membrane of the particle prevents substrate getting in or enzyme getting out. Even if, in the case of acid phosphatase, one raises the concentration of the β-glycerophosphate, the enzyme still remains inert. The location of the different enzymes among the particles of rat liver is summarized in Table 5.1.

TABLE 5.1. THE DISTRIBUTION OF ENZYMES AMONG THE DIFFERENT SUBCELLULAR COMPONENTS

Distribution	Enzymes
Mitochondrial	Cytochrome oxidase, rhodanase, succinate-cyt-c reductase, dehydrogenases (glutamate, malate, β-hydroxybutyrate) alkaline DNase
Microsomal	Glucose 6-phosphatase, esterase (aryl-sulphatase c)
Complex Mit.-micr.	NADH-cyt. c reductase, NADPH-cyt. c reductase, monoamine oxidase
Lysosomes	Acid phosphatase, cathepsin, acid RNase, acid DNase, β-glucuronidase, β-N-acetyl-deoxyglucosidase, β-galactosidase, a-mannosidase, a-glucosidase (aryl sulphatases A and B, phosphoprotein phosphatase, phosphatidate phosphatase)
Microbodies	Urate oxidase, catalase, D-amino acid oxidases

From C. de Duve, CIBA Symposium.

Latency also occurs in microbodies but here it is of a different type to that of the lysosomes because they are much more difficult to disrupt. The latency for catalase is not easy to explain for here the substrate is H_2O_2 and there is reason to believe that the membrane is permeable to this substance. The metabolic turnover of catalase is extremely high so that all the catalase in liver is replaced every 2 days.

Higashi and Peters[30] have studied the site in the liver cell of the synthesis of catalase by injecting a rat with [14C] leucine and then isolating the catalase from the subcellular fractions. They found that at short times after injection the catalase isolated from the fractions rich in fragments of the rough endoplasmic reticulum was much more radioactive than that from the mitochondrial fraction. They concluded that catalase was synthesized by the ribosomes of the rough endoplasmic reticulum. The most likely explanation of this result is that the microbodies containing catalase arise from the rough endoplasmic reticulum in a manner similar to the zymogen granules of the pancreas (see Chapter III). Unlike the zymogen granules the microbodies are retained in the cell.

Kidney Droplets

Strauss[11] has studied the so-called droplets in rat kidney and has shown that their enzymic composition is very similar to that of lysosomes of liver. He also showed that if the rat was first given an intraperitoneal injection of egg-white or horse-radish peroxidase, then the droplets subsequently isolated also contained a relatively high concentration of these foreign proteins. These findings suggested a relationship between lysosomes and the segregation or pinocytosis of foreign proteins. The peroxidase experiments have also proved useful in studying the location of the droplets since this enzyme is not normally present in animal cells so that a cytochemical reaction with benzidine may be used. As a result of this work Strauss called some of the particles phagosomes (phagocytic vacuoles). He has studied the relationship between phagosomes and lysosomes by using the peroxidase reaction for the former and acid phosphatase for the latter. He shows that at early stages after injection of peroxidase the lysosomes and phagosomes are separate in the cells of the kidney and liver but that at later stages they are combined. The liver cells that are studied in this work are not the parenchymal cells

but the Kupffer cells which, as mentioned in Chapter 1, are phagocytic in nature. We shall see that fusion of the phagosomes with lysosomes seems to take place in many types of cells active in pinocytosis
or phagocytosis.

Polymorphonuclear Leucocytes during Phagocytosis

Hirsch and Cohn[12] of the Rockefeller Institute in New York
have studied the phagocytic action of the white blood cells. These
cells are of various types the polymorphonuclear (PMN) leucocytes
having a nucleus with a particularly characteristic irregular multi-
lobed configuration. The PMN leucocytes are able to engulf and
destroy a wide variety of micro-organisms, but until recently little
was known concerning the chain of reactions leading to the intracellular inactivation and subsequent degradation of bacteria.

The PMN leucocytes are amoeboid cells which are normally
produced in the bone marrow where they mature then circulate in
the vascular system for a short time and enter the tissues in response
to inflammatory stimuli. During maturation, marked changes occur
in the distribution of cytoplasmic structures. Electron micrographs
have shown the progressive loss of mitochondria and endoplasmic
reticulum and the appearance of electron-dense granules. Hence
a striking morphological property of the cytoplasm of adult leucocytes when they enter the blood stream is the presence of numerous
characteristically staining granules. Hirsch and Cohn[13] have isolated
these granules from rabbit leucocytes by differential centrifugation
after breaking the cells osmotically. One of the most interesting
properties of the isolated granules is their sensitivity to pH, so
that they are stable in neutral or slightly alkaline solution but lyse
at pH values belows 6·0.

When the enzyme composition of the granules was determined it
was found that they were rich in acid hydrolases such as acid phosphatase, nucleotidase, ribonuclease, deoxyribonuclease and β-
glucuronidase. They also found the enzyme latency of the de Duve
lysosomes. The granules also contained the bacteriocidal agent
phagocytin.

They then found that there was a marked reduction in the number of cytoplasmic granules in both rabbit and human leucocytes following ingestion of various micro-organisms or a yeast cell preparation.[14] The degranulation followed within 30 min of phagocytosis and was directly related to the quantity of material engulfed. Thus the granules release the various digestive enzymes into the cytoplasm or into vacuoles following ingestion of foreign material. They showed too that engulfment of micro-organisms led to a progressive decrease in the activity of hydrolases which could be released from the granules with a concomitant increase in the activity of these enzymes in the supernatant. There was no significant difference in the total enzyme content of control and phagocytosing cells.[15]

The degranulation process has been studied by phase-contrast cinematography[16] which has established that it is an explosive event occurring within 0·1 sec and that it occurs only when the granules are in proximity to the ingested particle or in an area where another granule has ruptured. The ingested particle is a phagosome which has a limiting membrane so that it is probably this structure which the granule encounters prior to rupture. The exact mechanism of degranulation is still a subject of study.

Cohn postulates that the adult leucocyte is unable to form new granules after phagocytosis so that it may be considered an expendable end cell which discharges its functions and is then destroyed. In bacterial infection, the pus which accumulates under certain circumstances is composed almost entirely of dead leucocytes.

Lysosomes and Glycogenesis

Hers of Louvain has made an intensive study of a hereditary disease which is of particular interest to us in that it seems to be one of the few known hereditary clinical conditions attributed to the malfunction of an organelle. The term "glycogen-storage disease" covers a group of congenital hereditary diseases characterized by an abnormal accumulation of glycogen in tissues. Several forms can be recognized from their clinical manifestations and a greater variety is revealed by the biochemical analysis of tissues.

A particularly severe form of the disease is known as Pompe's disease and this causes the death of the patient during the first years of life. Hers has found that in normal liver there is present an α-glucosidase or maltase (an enzyme which degrades glycogen to maltose) but that this is absent in Pompe's disease.[17] There is a clear correlation between the absence of acid maltase in liver and heart and skeletal muscle and the large deposition of glycogen in these tissues that characterizes the disease.

Hers has made a study of the localization of the different α-glucosidases that occur in liver[18] and finds that the acid maltase described above is localized in the lysosomes while a neutral maltase occurs in both the soluble and microsomal fractions. Further studies showed that acid maltase had all the characteristics of a lysosomal enzyme. It has been shown that there is no important modification in the concentration of liver oligosaccharides in Pompe's disease and this suggests that acid maltase is not involved in the metabolism of these compounds. However, if glycogen were to enter vacuoles in which the normal glycogenolytic enzymes, such as phosphorylase, had been destroyed by the lysosomal hydrolases, then in the absence of acid maltase glycogen would accumulate. Since the first symptoms of Pompe's disease are only noticed a few months after birth Hers suggests that the pathological manifestations are not due to the enzymic defect itself but rather to the progressive glycogen deposition which causes the disruption of the muscular fibres. These conclusions are supported from the electron micrographs of the liver of a child with Pompe's disease which show that in sharp contrast to what has been described in other forms of glycogenesis the glycogen is mainly concentrated in granules that are surrounded by a membrane.[19]

Action of Vitamin A on the Stability of Lysosomes

This work was based on an observation of Fell and Mellanby[20] that when embryonic cartilage was grown in a medium containing an excess of vitamin A metachromatic material was progressively lost from the matrix which rapidly disintegrated. It was then shown that some of the gross effects of vitamin A could be duplicated by treatment of the rudiments with the proteolytic enzyme papain.[21] Furthermore, treatment of the rudiments under certain conditions caused the release of a proteolytic enzyme. The enzyme concerned was found in a particulate form in the tissue and seemed to be of lysosomal origin.

Dingle[22] collaborating with Fell then isolated lysosomes from rat liver and showed that the vitamin had a direct action on them in that it released a protease. The specificity of action of the vitamin on both isolated lysosomes and on the cartilagenous rudiments in culture was studied. In general the specific activity was very similar in the two systems.[23] It was postulated, therefore, that the vitamin acted directly on the lysosomes *in vivo* and many experiments have since confirmed this thesis.

In order to study the way in which vitamin A affects the stability of the lysosomes Dingle and Lucy[24] have investigated its effect on red blood cells and shown it to be a potent haemolytic agent. It also causes mitochondrial swelling.[25] That the vitamin has a direct action on lipoprotein membranes was shown by studying its effect on lecithin and cholesterol monolayers.[26] Even at low concentration the vitamin penetrated and expanded the film at an air/water interface. From these results it seems probable that the primary action of the vitamin upon the lysosomal particle is the penetration and expansion of the lipoprotein membrane.

It is interesting that the only form of the vitamin which was inactive in the above experiments was the ester of vitamin A alcohol. It is in this form that the vitamin is stored in the liver so that it must be relatively harmless under *in vivo* conditions, but presumably the alcohol may be released when and where required.

The Breakdown of Thyroglobulin

Thyroglobulin is made in the epithelial cells of the thyroid gland and is then secreted into the lumen of the follicle where it is present as colloid. The structure of the thyroid gland is shown schematically in Fig. 5.2. Thyroglobulin itself is a very large glycoprotein and very little of it gets into the plasma. The active thyroid hormones are thyroxine and tri-iodothyronine which are derived from thyroglobulin.

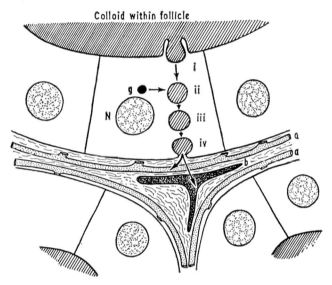

FIG. 5.2. Diagrammatic representation of the breakdown of thyroglobin in the thyroid gland. (i) Phagocytosis of colloid to form PAS positive vesicle. (ii) Transference of hydrolytic enzymes from dense granule (g). (iii) Digestion of colloid with progressive loss of PAS positive material. (iv) Extrusion of digestion products; iodothyronines pass mainly to the thyroid blood capillary (a) while undigested thyroglobulin is carried away via the lymphatic capillary (b). N: nucleus.

It has been known for some time that if a thyroid gland is stimulated by injection of pituitary thyroid stimulating hormone, droplets containing colloid are seen in the epithelial cells. The question has arisen as to the origin of such droplets. By staining sections of the gland for the enzyme acid phosphatase before and after stimulation and also by the periodic acid–Schiff reaction (PAS) which is positive for carbohydrate (i.e. for thyroglobulin since it is a glycoprotein) the probable sequence of events has become clearer. Present ideas are based mainly on the work of the American endocrinologist Wollman[27] and are shown diagrammatically in Fig. 5.2.

Granules containing acid phosphatase occur around the nucleus of the epithelial cells. These granules are probably lysosomes. The droplets near the apical membrane react only to PAS and hence are phagosomes containing colloid derived from the lumen. Particles towards the middle of the cell contain both PAS positive material and acid phosphatase whereas those near the base contain only acid phosphatase. The phagosomes, therefore, during their passage receive enzymes from the lysosomes. Possibly, as in the kidney, the two kinds of particle join, but this has not been shown. The hydrolytic enzymes of the lysosomes then break down the colloid so that by the time the particles reach the intravascular space no colloid is left. Presumably, thyroxine and tri-iodothyronine escape into the plasma, and any thyroglobulin remaining is taken up by the lymphatic capillary as shown by Roitt.[28].

The above is a very nice example of the way in which phagocytosis and the lysosomes work together to perform a most important physiological function.

The Intracellular Digestive Tract

Having described how lysosomes came to be isolated and their general properties and then five quite separate biological phenomena in which we believe lysosomes or their analogues are the common link we must put forward a unifying theory which fits most of the facts. De Duve[29] classifies the lysosomes into four distinct categories, storage granules, digestive vacuoles, autophagic vacuoles and residual bodies. The storage granules are lysosomes which are thought not yet to have been engaged in intracellular digestive processes. The components of the so-called intracellular digestive tract are shown in Fig. 5.3.

The storage granules are thought to arise from the endoplasmic reticulum, but this has not been definitely shown. To the extent that they may be likened to zymogen granules this seems a reasonable proposition. Novikoff believes that they pass through the Golgi complex which is indicated with a question mark in Fig. 5.3. The fusion of the phagosome and granule has not been shown in all cases but that it can arise has been demonstrated by Strauss in the

INTRACELLULAR DIGESTIVE TRACT

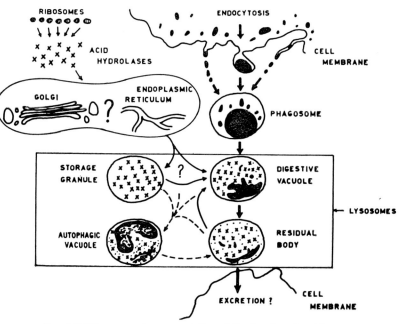

FIG. 5.3. Diagrammatic representation of the four functional forms covered by the lysome concept and of their interrelationships. (From C. de Duve, CIBA Symposium.)

kidney. Autophagic vacuoles have been seen in many cases and Porter recently reports that he has seen vacuoles containing pieces of mitochondria in rat liver. The only particle not included in the term lysosome is the phagosome which does not itself appear to have any hydrolytic enzymes. The reasons for the name "intracellular digestive tract" should now be apparent. In many ways the processes shown in Fig. 5.3 mimic those that go on in an animal with a digestive system. Material is taken in and broken down by hydrolytic enzymes and other substances and materials are excreted. In an animal such as an *Amoeba*, which has no well-differentiated digestive system, the food has to be taken in by phagocytosis and is quickly broken down. Holter[2] and his colleagues in Copenhagen have studied this process for many years and it provides us with an apparently very simple example of the intracellular digestive tract. In this case the way in which the hydrolytic enzymes arise in the phagosomes remains a mystery.

References

1. W. H. LEWIS, Pinocytosis, *Bull. Johns Hopk. Hosp.*, **49**, 17–26 (1931).
2. H. HOLTER, "Pinocytosis" in Functional biochemistry of cell structures, (Ed. O. LINDBERG), *Proc. Vth Int. Congress Biochem.*, **2**, 248–56 (1963).
3. See CIBA Symposium in Further Reading, Chapter 5.
4. C. DE DUVE, B. C. PRESSMAN, R. GIANETTO, R. WATTIAUX and F. APPELMANS, Tissue fractionation studies 6, *Biochem. J.*, **60**, 604–17 (1955).
5. C. DE DUVE, The separation and characterization of subcellular particles, *Harvey Lectures*, **59**, 49–87 (1963–4).
6. P. BAUDHUIN, H. BEAUFAY and C. DE DUVE, Combined biochemical and morphological study of particulate fractions from rat liver. Analysis of preparations enriched in lysosomes or in particles containing urate oxidase, D-amino acid oxidase and catalase, *J. Cell Biol.*, **26**, 219–43 (1965).
7. See Chapter 1, ref. 2.
8. See CIBA Symposium.
9. See Further Reading, Chapter 1.
10. See Chapter 1 ref, 5.
11. W. STRAUSS, Cytochemical observations in the relationship between lysosomes and phagosomes in kidney and liver by combined staining for acid phosphatase and intravenously injected horseradish peroxidase, *J. Cell. Biol.*, **20**, 497–507 (1964).
12. See CIBA Symposium.
13. Z. A. COHN and J. G. HIRSCH, The isolation and properties of the specific cytoplasmic granules of rabbit polymorphonuclear leucocytes, *J. exp. Med.*, 1960, **112**, 983–1004 (1960).
14. J. G. HIRSCH and Z. A. COHN, Degranulation of polymorphonuclear leucocytes following phagocytosis of micro-organisms, *J. exp. Med.*, **112**, 1005–14 (1960).
15. Z. A. COHN and J. G. HIRSCH, The influence of phagocytosis on the intracellular distribution of granule-associated components of polymorphonuclear leucocytes, *J. exp. Med.*, **112**, 1015–22 (1960).

16. J. G. HIRSCH, Cinemicrophotographic observations on granule lysis in polymorphonuclear leucocytes during phagocytosis, *J. exp. Med.*, **116**, 827–34 (1962).

17. H. G. HERS, α-Glucosidase deficiency in generalized glycogen storage disease (Pompe's disease), *Biochem. J.*, **86**, 11–16 (1963).

18. N. LEJEUNE, D. THINÈS-SEMPOUX and H. G. HERS, Tissue fractionation studies 16, *Biochem. J.*, **86**, 16–21 (1963).

19. P. BAUDHUIN, H. G. HERS and H. LOEB, An electron microscopic and biochemical study of type II glycogenosis, *Lab. Invest.* **13**, 1139–52 (1964).

20. H. B. FELL and E. MELLANBY, The effect of hypervitaminosis A on embryonic limb-bones cultivated *in vitro*, *J. Physiol. (Lond.)*, **116**, 320 (1952).

21. H. B. FELL and L. THOMAS, Comparison of the effects of papain and vitamin A on cartilage, *J. exp. Med.*, **111**, 719–44 (1960).

22. J. T. DINGLE, Studies on the mode of action of excess of Vitamin A. 3, *Biochem. J.*, **79**, 509–12 (1961).

23. H. B. FELL, J. T. DINGLE and M. WEBB, Studies on the mode of action of excess of Vitamin A. 4, *Biochem. J.*, **83**, 63 9 (1962).

24. J. T. DINGLE and J. A. LUCY, Studies on the mode of action of excess of vitamin A. 5, *Biochem. J.*, **84**, 611–21 (1962).

25. J. A. LUCY, M. LUSCOMBE and J. T. DINGLE, Studies on the mode of action of excess of vitamin A. 6, *Biochem. J.*, **89**, 419–25 (1963).

26. See CIBA Symposium.

27. S. H. WOLLMAN, S. S. SPICER and M. S. BURSTONE, Localization of esterase and acid phosphatase in granules and colloid droplets in rat thyroid epithelium. *J. Cell Biol.*, **21**, 191–201 (1964).

28. I. M. ROITT, P. DANIEL, O. PRATT and G. TORRIGIANI, unpublished observations; I. M. ROITT, K. J. BALLARD, S. J. HOLT, D. DONIACH, G. TORRIGIANI and C. SHAPLAND, Histochemical localisation of pH 3·5 protease in the human thyroid gland, *Proc. Int. Thyroid Conference, Rome*, 1965.

29. See CIBA Symposium.

30. T. HIGASHI and T. PETERS, jun., Studies on rat liver catalase II. Incorporation of ^{14}C–leucine into catalase of liver cell fractions *in vivo*, *J. biol. Chem.*, **238**, 3952–4 (1963).

Further Reading

C. DE DUVE, The separation and characterization of subcellular particles, *Harvey Lectures*, **59**, 49–87 (1963–4).

C. DE DUVE, Lysosomes, a new group of cytoplasmic particles in "Subcellular particles", *Amer. Physiol. Soc.*, 128–59 (1959).

C. DE DUVE, J. BERTHET and H. BEAUFAY, Gradient centrifugation of cell particles, theory and applications, *Progr. in Biophys. Biophysical Chem.*, **9**, 325–69 (1959).

Lysosomes, CIBA Foundation Symposium, J. &. A. Churchill, London, 1963. In this volume the following chapters are of particular pertinence.

C. DE DUVE, The lysosome concept.

A. B. NOVIKOFF, Lysosomes in the physiology and pathology of cells: contributions of staining methods.

Z. A. COHN, J. G. HIRSCH and E. WIENER, The cytoplasmic granules of phagocytic cells and the degradation of bacteria.

W. STRAUSS, Comparative observations on lysosomes and phagosomes in kidney and liver of rats after administration of horse-radish peroxidase.

J. T. DINGLE, Action of vitamin A on the stability of lysosomes *in vivo* and *in vitro*.

Separation of subcellular structural components, *Biochem. Soc. Symp.*, **23** (1963).

C. DE DUVE, The lysosome, *Scientific American*, May 1963.

CHAPTER 6

Conclusions and Future Developments

IN PREVIOUS chapters I have described the concepts and facts upon which the many scientists now engaged on research in this field base their experiments. In this last chapter it may be useful to consider the direction that this research effort is taking so that the reader may more easily detect the thread of progress in the enormous flood of research reports.

Methodology

In Chapter 1 we were concerned with methods for observing the cell and its components by electron microscopy and cytochemistry and for the isolation of subcellular components after disruption of the cell.

The present electron microscopes have a resolving power which is at least 500 times better than that of the light microscope. The ultimate limit of resolution of the electron microscope would make it 1000 times better than the light microscope but progress towards this objective is likely to be slow.[1] In the main, improvements in instrumentation are concerned with the simplification of operating techniques so that good results can be obtained without a profound knowledge of the construction of the microscope.

The major problem in the application of electron microscopy to the analysis of the fine structure of cells remains that of ensuring that the morphology of the living cell is faithfully retained in the dry section examined in the microscope. In most of the work so far described the material was fixed with osmium tetroxide. More recently there have been important developments in fixatives and in particular glutaraldehyde has given excellent results. According to Porter[2] the elucidation of the detailed structure of the sarcoplasmic reticulum of muscle depended on the use of this new fixative and no doubt there will be many similar developments in the future.

Many of the advances in protein chemistry have depended on the use of a technique known as freeze-drying in which proteins are dried from aqueous solutions in their frozen state. In this way the tertiary structure of the protein is retained. Since it is necessary for transmission electron microscopy to prepare a dry specimen for examination there have in the past been many methods based on the principle of freeze-drying. A recent development is that of freeze-etching[3] which has been used to study the structure of the inner membrane of fractured but unfixed mitochondria within frozen cells.

We have already mentioned some of the results obtained by the application of cytochemical techniques for the localization of enzymes in cells. An example of a recent development in this field is that by Lewis for the detection of cholinesterase.[4] This technique which utilizes esters of thiocholine as substrates can be made highly specific for true and for pseudocholinesterase and has been successfully applied to a study by electron microscopy of the fine structure of the region of the motor end plate and the cell bodies of the motor neurones. This method promises to have a profound influence on our knowledge of the structure and function of nerve tissue as does also the recent success of Whittaker[5] and his colleagues in the isolation of various subcellular components from this tissue.

We explained in Chapter 1 that during the process of cell disruption prior to the isolation of subcellular constituents by differential centrifugation some of the components of the cell are damaged. Attempts are now under way to try and reduce such damage by incorporating fixatives in the media used for homogenization. Thus by the use in this way of glutaraldehyde it is possible to detect in suspensions of disrupted cells the intact Golgi complex. It remains to be seen to what extent the presence of the fixative jeopardizes any chances of studying the chemistry of such isolated cell components. If these difficulties can be overcome, it may be possible to determine the morphological significance of the soluble enzymes found in suspensions of disrupted cells. Are those enzymes really present in the cytoplasm of the cell in a soluble form or have they been extracted from various structural components during the process of homogenization?

The technique of density gradient centrifugation for the separation of various constituents from a suspension of disrupted cells was described in Chapter 1 and we later saw many examples of the use of this valuable method. One of the disadvantages of this technique has been the small quantity of the material that can be isolated. To some extent this difficulty is being overcome by the use of larger swinging-bucket rotors but an entirely new method gives great promise. This is the method of zonal ultracentrifugation devised by Anderson.[6] In this method the usual buckets are replaced by a drum vertically divided into four equal sectors in which a density gradient is formed from the centre core to the outside. The sample is introduced into the core and the constituents distributed throughout the gradient by rotating the drum. Fractions from the gradient are then collected by pumping a dense solution into the drum behind the gradient. By this means a resolution as good as that obtained by conventional methods in the preparative ultracentrifuge is achieved but the capacity is increased by about 360 times. It is thus possible to recover in reasonable quantity "trace" constituents from cells and a recent example is the isolation of relaxing particles from rat skeletal muscle.[7] It may also be possible to isolate viruses either from tissue extracts or even from blood.

Structure and Function of Cell Components

In Chapter 2 the endoplasmic reticulum and the ribosomes were considered. Our knowledge of the chemistry and physical chemistry of both these components is at present limited. Much discussion continues on the nature of the various membranes in the cell but progress has been hindered by the difficulty of isolating them in a form that bears a reasonable resemblance to their state in the living cell.

While much has been learnt about the structure of small viruses, progress on the structure of ribosomes has been much less impressive. In this respect ribosomes isolated from animal cells seem to exist in many more shapes and sizes than do those from bacteria. There is at present little indication of the physiological significance of this phenomenon.

In the field of protein synthesis there remain so many problems that it is hard to be selective but three may be chosen as being particularly relevant to our present subject. In cells that synthesize protein both for their own activity and for export the problem of segregation of the two types of functional protein is important. Some work suggests that in a cell such as the parenchymal cell of the liver all the protein is synthesized by the ribosomes bound to the rough endoplasmic reticulum and that the types of functional protein are segregated in the Golgi complex.[8] It remains possible, however, that the two types of protein are synthesized on morphologically distinct polysomes. This raises the second point which is the relationship of the components of the microsome fraction active in protein synthesis with the structures present in the living cell. Progress in this field is likely to depend on the careful correlation of the results of many different kinds of experiments. Finally, there is the control of protein synthesis assuming that the appropriate messenger RNA's are available for the synthesis of the proteins. Until recently, it has been believed that the rate of synthesis of a protein depended on the amount of m-RNA available. It is now apparent that m-RNA in differentiated animal cells is metabolically too stable to fulfil this function and, moreover, the rate of synthesis may be altered by agents such as hormones under conditions where there is no synthesis of m-RNA. There is increasing evidence that the rate of protein synthesis in animal cells is affected by controlling the rate of translation of the information contained in m-RNA. There is, as yet, little evidence concerning the mechanism of this control mechanism.

In Chapter 5 the concept of enzyme latency and the role of lysosomes was discussed. This remains a particularly active field and Allison[9] has recently reviewed some current developments. He is particularly concerned with the way in which toxic dusts, such as silica, kill cells, which is important industrially. The first effect of silica ingestion is the death of the macrophages that take up the mineral in the lungs. The silica causes the release of lysosomal enzymes into the cytoplasm of the macrophages resulting in the death and dissolution of the cells. The silica particles remain to be taken up again and kill other cells and so a cycle of death continues which in turn starts off the deposition of fibrous tissue.

Allison has also found that lysosomes are sensitive to oxygen concentration so that if cells or organs are exposed to environments containing either too much or too little oxygen, lysosomal enzymes are released. This work may well be relevant to the severe damage to the brain caused by oxygen lack.

It has been estimated that 40% of the contents of a liver cell consist of membranes so that it may be appropriate to give prominence to the membranes at the close of this chapter. It is possible to isolate cell membranes from disrupted cells by density gradient centrifugation[10] and Epstein and Holt[11] have demonstrated the metabolic activity of these membranes by a cytochemical method that detects the presence of surface enzymes splitting ATP. They worked with HeLa cells before and after infection with Herpes simplex virus and found that under both conditions about half the cells showed enzyme activity. The activity was confined to the areas of the cell membrane containing microvilli and was absent from the smooth surfaces. It was shown that the virus particles escape from the cells and mature by budding out through cellular membranes, carrying in the process a portion of the latter on to themselves to form the outer vital limiting membrane. It is to be hoped that by a combination of the many methods now available there will be rapid progress in our understanding of the chemistry, activity and origin of the membranes of the cell.

In this book it has been necessary to be selective and to pick out from a vast field certain subjects for closer examination. In the process the impression may have been given that cells consist of several constituents each functioning in isolation. Nothing could be further from the truth, for the great wonder of all living tissues and cells is the incredible co-ordination of their complex reactions. The experimental approach often has, of necessity, to focus attention on one aspect of cell activity but the scientist who does not attempt to fit his results into the pattern of the whole cell fails to appreciate his ultimate objective.

References

1. E. RUSKA, Current efforts to attain the resolution limit of the transmission electron microscope, *J. roy. Micr. Soc.*, **84**, 77–103 (1965).
2. K. R. PORTER and C. FRANZINI-ARMSTRONG, The sarcoplasmic reticulum, *Scientific American*, March 1965.
3. H. MOOR, C. RUSKA and H. RUSKA, Elektroenmikroskopische Darstellung tierischer Zellen mit den Gefrieratz-technik, *Z. Zellforsch*, **62**, 581–601 (1964).
4. P. R. LEWIS and C. C. D. SHUTE, *J. Anat. Lond.*, **99**, 941 (1965).
5. V. P. WHITTAKER, Chapter 1, ref. 3.
6. N. G. ANDERSON, Chapter 1, ref. 8.
7. H. SCHUEL, L. LORAND, R. SCHUEL and N. G. ANDERSON, Isolation of relaxing particles from rat skeletal muscle in zonal ultracentrifuge, *J. gen. Physiol*, **48**, 737 (1965).
8. C. BRUNI and K. R. PORTER, Chapter 1, ref. 2.
9. A. C. ALLISON, The lysosome, *Discovery*, **26** (7), 8–13 (1965).
10. D. M. NEVILLE, The isolation of a cell membrane fraction from rat liver, *J. Cell Biol.*, **8**, 413–22 (1960).
11. M. A. EPSTEIN and S. J. HOLT, Electron microscopic observations on the surface adenosine triphosphatase-like enzymes of HeLa cells injected with Herpes virus, *J. Cell Biol.*, **19**, 337–47 (1963).

Index